COMMUNITY DEVELOPMENT IN HEALTH & SOCIAL SERVICES

The Craigavon and Banbridge Experience

SOCIAL
SERVICES
NSPECTORATE

Published by: Craigavon and Banbridge Community Health & Social Services Trust
Bannvale House
10 Moyallen Road
GILFORD
BT63 5JX
Northern Ireland
Tel: 028 38831983

Co-Sponsor: Social Services Inspectorate, Department of Health & Social Services

Produced by the Community Work Team, Brownlow Health & Social Services Centre
1 Legahory Centre, Brownlow, Craigavon, Northern Ireland BT65 5BE

First published September 1999

ISBN 0 9536959 0 5

Craigavon and Banbridge Community H&SS Trust is an NHS Trust.

The views expressed in this publication are the authors' and not necessarily those of
Craigavon & Banbridge Community H&SS Trust or the Social Services Inspectorate,
Department of Health & Social Services.

Layout and design by Andrea Buckley.
Cover designed by Jayne McBeigh, Tel: 028 9068 2523
Printed by James Hamilton & Co (Lurgan), Craigavon.

Contents

Foreword

Community workers have been employed within the Craigavon and Banbridge areas for twenty five years. Within the last decade community workers have consolidated their position and have increasingly been recognised as making a meaningful and relevant contribution towards the core business of the Trust. Community development has now been recognised as a useful method across all programmes of care. The Community Work Team is seen as playing a pivotal role in building relationships between statutory, voluntary and community sectors.

On reflection, in 1990 many influences came together which undoubtedly shaped and directed the emergence of the value of community work and community development approaches to service delivery. Managers and fellow professionals were subject to challenging organisational change at the same time.

The integrated health and social care structures in Northern Ireland since 1973 had not realised their potential, and corporate responsibilities linked with executive professional lines of accountability resulted in little sharing of vision, responsibility or changed ways of working. General Management introduced at Unit of Management level in 1990 created the separation within Craigavon and Banbridge, of acute and community services. Our Trust strongly supports such separation, a view shared by sister community Trusts as it has allowed a focus on community services without the acute hospital dominating the agenda, which has been my experience of combined acute and community management units.

The changing work environment included new management arrangements to maximise integration of health and social care, the beginning of the purchaser/provider split in service delivery, and the whole mixed economy of community care post Griffiths. Increased emphasis was placed on user involvement, a needs rather than a service led model at a time of year after year cash releasing "efficiency saving". Interestingly, it was not until cash releasing began to cut deep into service provision, that a catalyst was provided to examine practice, look at value for money and promote changed working arrangements. The Trust was deeply involved in attracting and supporting the EU Poverty 3 Programme in Brownlow reported on by Norman Gillespie in his chapter.

These were defining days for community work and community development. The Trust community workers had been formed into a specialist team rather than isolated practitioners, with no input into strategic direction on service provision. For the first time they were recognised as being skilled in neighbourhood work, networking arrangements, needs analysis, alternative partnership models of meeting identified needs and increasing specialist knowledge of funding.

I like to think that hand in hand with the above developments, we were developing an increased awareness of the potential of a community development approach to some areas of our work and through practical examples the inter-related factors contributing to health and social gain.

I commend not only Martin O'Neill and his team, but also the many other managers and professionals within our Trust who have come to recognise the value of the community development approach. I would also like to acknowledge the voluntary sector and the energy, commitment and skills of the community we have sought to engage and serve. We now have a better shared understanding on tackling some of the problems being experienced by vulnerable individuals and communities.

Whilst the community development approach is not the panacea in all situations, it most definitely has its place within statutory health and social services working in partnership with communities and other statutory and voluntary agencies. The examples from practice will give readers a snapshot from some of our direct experiences, which I hope will contribute to the present debate on the implementation of Policy to Practice and mainstreaming community development across health and social services in Northern Ireland and elsewhere.

W Denis Preston
Chief Executive
Craigavon and Banbridge Community Health & Social Services Trust

Preface

I warmly welcome the publication of this book which celebrates so effectively the role of community work and community development within the Health and Social Services. It is an important, timely and valuable initiative by the Craigavon and Banbridge Community Health and Social Services Trust where, uniquely in Northern Ireland, community work has now been part of mainstream health and social services programmes for some 25 years.

This is an important publication for a number of reasons. It portrays innovative approaches directed by a well established focus on 'community' as a means of achieving and broadening the capacity for social change. This ethos is just now gaining renewed and increasing recognition throughout the health and social services. Community development is a means of helping people who feel excluded or marginalised by society for reasons that may be related to civic, economic, social, or interpersonal factors. Social Services engage every day with people in such circumstances and, like health professionals, have a long tradition of expertise in working with individuals and families. The 1993 Strategy for the Support of the Voluntary Sector and for Community Development, however, recognised that community development had the potential to make a major impact on a wide range of policies and programmes in both the statutory and voluntary sectors. It acknowledged the need to strengthen Departments' commitments to this approach. As part of its action to address this, the Voluntary Activity Unit published in 1996 two associated documents:

- 'Monitoring and Evaluation of Community Development in Northern Ireland', and

- 'Measuring Community Development in Northern Ireland – A Handbook for Practitioners'.

These contain a wealth of information which clarifies the role, values and principles of community development in the context of evaluation and measurement. Although applicable to a wide range of settings, they are important tools for health and social services agencies seeking to use community development as an approach to improve health and social gain. By sharing the practical experience of establishing community based initiatives, the projects presented in this publication by the Craigavon and Banbridge Trust provide yet another useful tool that, in this case, is 'ready made' for managers and practitioners in the health and social services.

'Well into 2000', the Government's vision for improving the health and wellbeing of the people of Northern Ireland, expresses the wish that community development will be extended and strengthened throughout Northern Ireland and mainstreamed in all health and social services agencies. Health and Social Services Boards are now required by Government to promote and employ community development and partnership approaches to target health and social need and to ensure that staff have access to education and training in these approaches. This book shows what can be done and provides a valuable historical, theoretical and practical framework for learning – all the more relevant because it is firmly grounded in local experience

'Well into 2000' also incorporates key principles of social inclusion, social justice and partnerships for health and wellbeing to guide, motivate and set a common direction for change in the health and social services. Social inclusion is about working towards a fairer, more participative and socially healthy society. Social justice is about tackling the many ways in which individuals and communities experience disadvantage and working with renewed commitment to reduce inequalities in health and social wellbeing. Positive partnerships are about stimulating and coordinating action by government, its agents and other organisations in the public, private and voluntary and community sectors. They are about enabling and securing the full participation of individuals and local communities in identifying and addressing their own needs and in making an impact on plans and policies that will affect them in the future. These principles are at the heart of community development. They are well demonstrated in the practice presented here which shows individuals, groups, and communities effectively engaged in tackling their own health and social concerns and working together with a wide range of agencies and professionals to achieve change.

Community development has also emerged as a significant strand in the Government's New Targeting Social Need initiative (New TSN). In November 1998, the Community Development Working Group, which was established as a sub-group of the DHSS Targeting Health and Social Need Steering Group produced its report 'Mainstreaming Community Development in the Health and Social Services' (DHSS, 1999). The report advised on how community development approaches might be encouraged, supported and expanded in progressing the Department's Targeting Health and Social Need initiative. Such is the importance of its recommendations that they have been included in the DHSS draft New TSN Action Plan, which will form part of the first New TSN Annual Report due to be published for consultation in September 1999.

The timeliness of this book is therefore evident – it deals with themes that are currently right at the centre of Government policies and shows how people and communities are already working these out in practice.

Finally, I commend the Craigavon and Banbridge Community H&SS Trust for its strong commitment to community development demonstrated over many years. I also pay tribute to the authors and the communities represented for sharing their valuable experience and thereby enabling us all to learn from it.

Dr Kevin McCoy CBE
Chief Inspector
Social Services Inspectorate
Department of Health and Social Services

Acknowledgements

The idea for a book about community development and the experience of agencies, practitioners and communities working together, was first aired by Martin O'Neill, Senior Community Worker in the Craigavon and Banbridge Community Health & Social Services Trust. The idea was taken up and encouraged by the Trust, which jointly with the Social Services Inspectorate (SSI) DHSS, supported the initiative by sponsoring the publication of this book. The authors are grateful for this support and in particular to Mr W Denis Preston, Chief Executive of the Trust who offered encouragement and guidance throughout and to Dr Hilary Harrison (SSI) who assisted the process by acting as our liaison with the Department.

Thanks are due to a number of people involved in producing and publishing the book. They include all the contributors, who, in addition to writing the chapters, attended an initial meeting to discuss the book and a Writers' Workshop.

Thanks also to the Editorial Team, made up of Martin O'Neill, Dr Liz McShane, independent consultant, Dr Jim Campbell, Lecturer in Social Work, Queen's University, Belfast, Edwin Graham, Director, Lurgan Council for Voluntary Action and Fergal O'Brien, Community Worker in Craigavon and Banbridge Community Health & Social Services Trust. The Editorial Team met several times to plan and oversee the work, to read and agree draft chapters and to share the tasks involved in publication, giving their time to fit the book into their existing work schedules. Andrea Buckley gave essential secretarial support, acted as the point of communication for all the contributors and editors, and kept people in touch with developments. She also played a key role in the process of preparing the book for printing and publishing. Thanks to all the voluntary organisations and community groups in the area.

Thanks are also due to Craigavon and Banbridge Community Health & Social Services Trust Directors, especially Mrs Rosaleen Moore, Director of Mental Health and Disability, Mrs Roisin Burns, Director of Elderly and Primary Care, Mr Louis Boyle, Director of Child and Family Care, Mr Colm Donaghy, Director of Business and Planning, Mr Kieran Donaghy, Director of Human Resources and Mr Ronnie Crozier, Director of Finance. We also wish to thank Non-Executive Directors, Ms Roisin McDonough, Ms Mary McPartland, Mr John Fairleigh, Mr Cyril McElhinney and Mr Michael Morrow and all Trust Managers and Staff.

Contributors' Details

Mel Byrne BA Dip SS MSW, CQSW, PQSW qualified as a Social Worker in 1989 from Queens University. From 1989 to 1991 he worked as a family and child care Social Worker in East Belfast. He then moved to the Craigavon area in 1991 to take up a post as Community Worker with the Craigavon and Banbridge Community Health & Social Services Trust. Since moving there he has continued to develop his social work skills and knowledge, in 1994 he qualified as a Practice Teacher and in 1998 he was awarded the Post Qualifying Certificate in Social Work.

Dr Jim Campbell worked as a mental health social worker before becoming a lecturer in Social Work at Queens University of Belfast. His teaching and research interests are in the fields of mental health social work, the role of the Approved Social Worker, social work and social policy, and social work and the social conflict in Northern Ireland. He has recently published in each of these areas.

Dr Alastair Chestnutt is a rural, single-handed General Practitioner working in Ballyward since 1988. He has been a member of Garran and Croob Cross Committee Association's Committee since its formation.

Janet Davidson BSc (Hons), RGN, NDNC, PWT, IHSC has been a District Nurse within Craigavon and Banbridge Community Health & Social Services Trust for some twenty years. She has been a District Nurse Team Leader since 1991 with management responsibility for the District Nursing Staff in the Garran and Croob area.

Alan Deane is a self-employed manager, providing GP management services at Ballyward and Rathfriland Surgeries. He entered the primary health care sector in 1994, following 23 years Engineering management and Total Quality Management career in British Telecom – at Level 1 and Executive Level 2. His present remit covers – people, IT, project, quality accreditation, community fundholding, pharmacy and business issues. Trained surveyor for the Health Quality Service in London and been privileged to attend DOG/NICARE's Russian Project Workshops in Samara.

Harry Douglas has worked in a range of settings as a professional Social Worker. He is a Social Work Trainer and Practice Teacher with the Southern Health & Social Board with teaching and research interests in social work, student learning and staff development.

Brian Drury worked as Placement and Access Officer with Craigavon and Banbridge Volunteer Bureau from January 1998 to November 1999, having previously worked for a number of charities in Northern Ireland and England. He is currently studying Occupational Psychology at Queen's University, Belfast with an aim to develop a career within the area of disability employment.

Dr Brid Farrell is a Consultant in Public Health Medicine in the Southern Health & Social Services Board, Northern Ireland. She qualified as a Doctor in 1982 and worked for three years as a General Practitioners before pursuing a career in public health medicine. She has been in her present post since October 1994 and her areas of special interest include: elderly services, maternal and child health services and disability.

Dr Norman Gillespie is Community Development Evaluator at Moylinn House Community Development Support Services Agency. He has extensive experience in the field of social research, specialising in community studies and social exclusion. He was Project Evaluator for the Third European Anti-Poverty Programme in Brownlow, Craigavon.

Ann Godfrey holds the post of Principal Social Worker, Children's Services Planning in the Southern Health & Social Services Board. Most of her career has been spent in statutory social work, including probation, child protection and mental health work. Ann has also been a social work trainer for the last seven years.

Patricia Gormley was the Project Manager/Development Officer for Away From Home and Safe. Away From Home and Safe works across Northern Ireland in partnership with local community and voluntary groups and Health & Social Services Boards and Trusts to develop local community initiatives which aim to protect children. This is achieved through the development of good child protection practices through the provision of locally provided training on child protection.

Edwin Graham is the Director of Lurgan Council for Voluntary Action. He is also Chairperson of the Craigavon District Partnership and a member of the Joint Government/Community and Voluntary Sector Forum.

Joan Green is a Health Visitor in Craigavon and Banbridge Community Health & Social Services Trust. She is aligned to a GP Practice and has worked at various levels with the Travelling community for nineteen years as a Health Visitor. She has been involved in targeting the health needs of this community. This work has been challenging, but it has been an enjoyable aspect of her career.

Liz Hanna has been an active member of the Garran and Croob Cross Community Association since June 1998. Her interest in community work began with Banbridge Gateway Club over a four year period, culminating in her undertaking a Certificate in Foundation Studies for Mature Students. Liz is about to undertake a Youth and Community Work Course in the University of Ulster at Jordanstown.

Nicola Hodge is currently employed by Banbridge District Council as the Economic Development Officer, developing programmes within the Local Economic Development Strategy. When she commenced employed with Banbridge District Council four years ago, she held the post of Community Economic Development Officer, working closely with Banbridge District's community groups.

Dr Philomena Horner is Co-ordinator of the Springwell Centre, Lurgan, a post she has held since 1993. She has been involved in community work for almost thirty years, first as a Youth Worker, and more recently, as Chairperson, then Secretary, of North Lurgan Community Association. She is Director of a number of community groups and designated Chair of LCVA for 1999-2000.

Eamonn Keenan (Dip. Youth Community Work and CQSW) has been a practitioner, trainer and evaluator both in Northern Ireland and abroad for over twenty years. He was previously Community Development Worker with the Garran and Croob Cross Community Association. He is currently employed as a Community Youth Worker in Belfast.

Jacquie Kilfeather is the Project Co-ordinator with the Southern Travellers' Early Years Partnership (STEP), based in Moylinn House Community Resource Centre, Craigavon, Northern Ireland. STEP is a partnership between the Traveller projects in the Southern Health & Social Services Board area. STEP support the work of the Traveller projects in their delivery of early years care and educational services, and co-ordinates a strategic response to these issues, highlighting Travellers' cultural needs and using a community development approach.

Stephen Lavery is the Part-time Development Officer for Friends and Carers Engaged (FACE) Mental Health Charity. His role is to promote the aims and objectives of FACE, which are to provide support, advice, assistance, training, respite care and mutual respect and understanding to the carers and families of people with severe mental ill health throughout the Craigavon and Banbridge locality. Recent relevant experience includes being a member of 'The Jag' Newsletter Editorial Team which has a readship of 2,500 throughout the local community.

Dr Kevin F McCoy began his social work career in the early 1960s with the County Down Welfare Committee. He joined the Department of Health & Social Services in 1972 and held a number of posts covering a range of subjects and issues. He was appointed Chief Inspector of the Social Services Inspectorate in 1989 and has a strategic interest in the development of services and approaches to meet the social care needs of the population.

Noel McElroy is employed by Craigavon and Banbridge Community Health & Social Services Trust as a Specialist Project Nurse, co-ordinating the 'Out & About Project', a project which provides psycho/social rehabilitation within the Craigavon and Banbridge locality. Having been involved with the Community Liaison Committee (CLC), 'The Jag' and Prejudice Reduction Roadshow from its inception up to what it is today, has given Noel an insight into what community development is, and a desire to continue working within this sphere of employment.

Dr Liz McShane is an independent researcher and consultant and carries out work for statutory, voluntary and community organisations, related to issues such as community development, work with women, families and children, Travellers, health and social services. She previously worked for the Northern Ireland Voluntary Trust and lectured in social policy at Queen's University, Belfast and the University of Ulster at Jordanstown.

Fergal O'Brien works as a Community Worker in Craigavon and Banbridge Community Health & Social Services Trust. He has been active in the field of community development for five years and is a Social Work Practice Teacher. He also has obtained the Post Qualifying Award in Social Work. He has three and a half years experience as a Youth and Community Worker with the Newry Travellers.

Liam O'Flaherty qualified as a Social Worker in 1983 and since then has held a number of social work posts in health care, generic social work and within the field of learning disability. He moved to his current position in Craigavon and Banbridge Community Health & Social Services Trust as Team Leader within the programme of care for Older Persons in 1991.

Martin O'Neill works as a Senior Community Worker in the Craigavon and Banbridge Community Health & Social Services Trust. He has been active in the field of community development for the past sixteen years and is involved in a range of projects in the Craigavon and Banbridge area. He is a Social Work Practice Teacher and also has obtained the Post Qualifying Award in Social Work.

W Denis Preston Qualified as a Social Worker in 1967. Appointed as District Social Services Officer in 1973 with Newry & Mourne District of the Southern Health & Social Services Board in charge of Personal Social Services.

Moved to Craigavon & Banbridge as Unit General Manager in 1990 and led the Unit into Trust Status in 1994 where he remains as Chief Executive.

Yvonne Spiers is currently employed as a Health Visitor with Craigavon and Banbridge Community Health & Social Services Trust. A considerable section of her caseload would include the Garran and Croob area. With regards to her role within the community group, she is a member of the Committee, and as such would contribute to issues concerning children under the age of five and the elderly.

Ruth Stewart is a Community Development Officer working with the Rural Community Network (Northern Ireland) based in Cookstown, Northern Ireland. Ruth worked for the Craigavon Travellers' Support Committee from 1995-1998 as a Community Development Worker. Both of these posts involve working with marginalised groups and Ruth uses the philosophy of community development in promoting self-reliance and self-help in disadvantaged communities.

Glossary

Agenda 21: An agenda for sustainable development arising from the Earth Summit 1992 addressing pressing problems of today and aiming to prepare the world for the challenges of the next century and detailing ways in which public participation can be supported by governments.

Capacity Building: Development work that strengthens the ability of community organisations and groups to build their structures, systems, people and skills so they are better able to define and achieve their objectives and engage in consultation and planning, manage community projects and take part in partnerships and community enterprises.

Community Action: Emphasises collective action by those adversely affected by policies entailing challenging the status quo and developing alternative strategies.

Community Care: Process of assessing needs, profiling communities, identifying unmet need, establishing support networks and contributing to planning, policy and practice within the fields of health and social care.

Community Development: Community Development is about the strengthening and bringing about change in communities. It consists of a set of methods which can broaden vision and capacity for social change and approaches, including consultation, advocacy and relationships with local groups. It is a way of working, informed by certain principles which seek to encourage communities - people who live in the same areas or who have something else in common - to tackle for themselves the problems which they face and identify to be important, and which aim to empower them to change things by developing their own skills, knowledge and experience, and also by working in partnerships with other groups and with statutory agencies.

Community Infrastructure: The community infrastructure is part of the environment within which community organisations operate. This includes resources, networking, participation structures, community development support and professional capacity building.

Community Organisation: Involves improving communication, co-ordination and collaboration between agencies delivering services within a local community.

Empowerment: Allows the individual/community to take control of their health and social needs.

EU Special Support Programme for Peace and Reconciliation: Major funding programme aimed at promoting peace and reconciliation in Northern Ireland which followed the 1994 Republican and Loyalist ceasefires.

European Union Structural Funds: European Funding Programme aimed at addressing inequalities in regional wealth.

Needs Assessment: Profiling to obtain community health and social needs, population views of health and social needs and to identify gaps in service delivery.

Purchasing Prospectus: Document published by local health and social services boards annually, outlining services it intends to purchase from health trusts, the local voluntary/community sector and independent sectors.

Targeting Health and Social Need Initiative (THSN): Government initiative aimed at improving social, health and economic conditions of disadvantaged people.

The Community Sector: The whole range of autonomous collective activity directly undertaken by individuals within their neighbourhood or community of interest to improve collective life and conditions.

Voluntary Activity Unit: (VAU) The Voluntary Activity Unit provides a focus within Government on voluntary activity, has lead responsibility for volunteering and for community development and facilitates closer liaison among Departments in these areas. The Unit is also responsible for charity law in Northern Ireland and for various domestic, European and International Fund for Ireland programmes, which provide financial support for the voluntary and community sector.

Voluntary Sector Organisations: Groups whose activities are carried out other than for profit but which are not public or local authorities. These organisations would normally be formally constituted and employ paid professional and administrative staff. They may or may not use volunteer help.

Introduction

Dr Liz McShane

This book explores the issue of introducing community development approaches into the work of statutory health and social services, within the area of the Craigavon and Banbridge Community Health & Social Services Trust. The Trust is publishing the book to promote debate on this aspect of current social policy; to highlight the value of a community development approach; to recognise the Trust's existing community development role; to record practice examples; to encourage replication in other areas and to discuss some of the benefits and limits of incorporating community development goals and methods into the setting and culture of statutory services. The book is a contribution to encourage the development of such approaches elsewhere in Northern Ireland, the UK, the Republic of Ireland and further afield.

The book is aimed primarily at organisations and people in the statutory, voluntary and community sectors, such as directors, managers, practitioners, user groups and self-help groups, who are carrying out or planning similar work. It will also be of use to students in the fields of social work, medicine, nursing, mental health and community work who may expect to work in a community setting.

Community development in some form has been sustained in Northern Ireland from the early 1970s, a period which saw the onset of 'The Troubles' and also urban redevelopment programmes, including the creation of Craigavon new town. The experience of the Craigavon and Banbridge Trust is unique, in that it is the only Trust in Northern Ireland which has had a community work presence as part of its mainstream structure and programmes from its inception in 1974, and a Community Work Team since 1990.

Community development is a concept with a range of interpretations. Chapter One *The Re-emergence of Community Development,* quotes from the DHSS Northern Ireland document 'Well Into 2000' (1997), which states that: *"Community development involves supporting local communities to identify the health and social concerns of greatest importance to them and helping them to devise and implement solutions. The Government wishes to see community development further extended, strengthened and promoted throughout Northern Ireland and mainstreamed in all Health & Social Services agencies.".*

The community development approach as described in this book embraces certain principles, goals and methods of work. Its values and methods include: empowerment, user and community involvement and participation, joint working or partnerships between professionals and service users, accessible, user-friendly services, a clear structure of accountability and an inclusive approach which works **with**, not for, people.

Community development programmes are not imposed from the top down, but include the users of services and members of local communities in joint activities with professionals and agencies. The aim is for those affected by policies and service provision to have a say in defining their own needs, and in the planning and delivery of more effective and beneficial services.

The book is in two parts, Part 1 has three chapters which provide a broad overview of the subject. It includes: the background of community development and community work in Northern Ireland and the context of its development in the Craigavon area.

Part 2 has nine chapters which look at the community development approach in eight areas of policy and practice. These are the work of the Craigavon and Banbridge Community Health & Social Services Trust Community Work Team; community development and inter-professional working in a rural general practice; a women's community health initiative; two examples of developing provision and services with Travellers in the area; an example of partnership working to promote good practice in community-based childcare; a supported volunteering project for people with disabilities; an example of joint working of a user group and mental health professionals; and the social firms model as an alternative to day centres.

Part 3, the Conclusion, summarises some of the main findings from Parts 1 and 2, relates the work to the current context of policy and practice of community development in Northern Ireland, and discusses future developments in the field.

The process of planning and compiling the book aimed to reflect the participatory ethos of the work. It involved informing Trust staff of the idea and calling a meeting of all those interested in contributing to the book to discuss its rationale and structure. From this meeting, an Editorial Team of five people was appointed to oversee the process and progress of the work. The Team arranged a Writer's Workshop for those interested in contributing to the book, facilitated by Jim Campbell from Queen's University Belfast, one of the Editorial Team. The contributors are all experienced community practitioners working in the statutory, voluntary and community sectors. All those involved in producing the book hope that it will be used by people working in similar fields, to help move forward the community development approach into mainstream services and hence increase the quality, accessibility and responsiveness of those services.

Reference

Department of Health & Social Services (1997) Well Into 2000, DHSS, Belfast.

1 The Re-emergence of Community Development

Martin O'Neill and Harry Douglas

Introduction

This chapter sets out to document the re-emergence of community development as a vibrant, creative and legitimate activity within the broad spectrum of the voluntary sector, social work, social care and health provision, and so promote community development in contemporary practice. An examination of its demise from what Popple (1995) described as a *"... golden age of community work from the mid-1960s until the mid/late-1970s ..."* , to its re-discovery in the 1990s, will hopefully shed light on the cocktail of political, social and organisational influences which impinge on this particular method of working in a pivotal position between the State and local communities. Community development is used as a generic term which encompasses Popple's (1995) definition of community work, community care and community organisation. Our purpose is therefore to contend that community development, in its variety of statutory and voluntary forms, is in a unique position because of its theoretical, skills and value bases, to make a meaningful contribution to contemporary society in Northern Ireland at a time of dramatic political, social and economic change.

There are as many definitions of what 'community development' is as there are books written on the topic. Authors such as Dominelli (1990) see it as a set of ideas, a radical social movement. Others such as Baldock (1977) regard it as an activity of engaging with local communities who are often disadvantaged, marginalised and oppressed, within a more global social welfare model of service provision. Community development, therefore, sits in a tense position between a radical model of collective community action, and a more consensual approach based on the premise of mediation between the State and local communities. 'Paid', or professional community work, is financed almost exclusively by government at EU, regional and local levels. It therefore falls more easily into the consensus model. Taylor and Presley (1987) have described this work as being dedicated to increasing the expertise, capacity and control of non-professionals, who are often in difficult or disadvantaged circumstances. In these terms then, 'community development' is best defined by what community workers do. Popple (1995) provides a useful model which identifies eight major areas of community work activity, ranging from involvement in cultivating community care networks, to challenging discrimination and oppression. This framework will be used later on in this Chapter to examine how community workers operate in contemporary practice settings.

Figure 1	<u>Models of Community Work Practice</u>
	1. Community Development
	2. Community Care
	3. Community Action
	4. Community Education
	5. Community Relations
	6 Feminist Community Work
	7. Community Organisation
	8. Community Service

Any discussion of community development must recognise that this method of working with and in communities is not apolitical. It can, indeed, be viewed from diverse political positions. Those on the Right can lend it support because of its self-help ethos and the link with self-determination. For those of a more radical and Left-of-centre perspective, community development can be supported because of its role in countering structural inequality. In these terms, writers such as Gough (1992) perceive it as a means to assist the addressing of inequalities in the structures of society and the tackling of issues such as racial, gender and sectarian discrimination. Proponents of each political ideology also have suspicions of community development - the Right view it as a potential vehicle for pursuing a radical hidden agenda (see Naidoo and Wills, 1994), while the Left perceive that it can be used to placate communities, and that it can be used as a subtle means of social control (see Gough, 1992).

Community Development in Health and Social Services: Towards 2000
The Incorporation of 'Well Into 2000' and 'Fit for the Future'

"History shows that the most successful societies are those that harness the energies of voluntary action, giving due recognition to the third sector of voluntary and community organisations." (The Active Community speech by Prime Minister Tony Blair at the Annual Conference of NCVO, 2 January 1999.)

In its Regional Strategy for Health and Social Wellbeing in Northern Ireland 1997-2002, (DHSS 1996), the Department of Health & Social Services acknowledged that community development has a strong role to play in providing positive health and social wellbeing. The interplay of social, cultural, economic and environmental factors on health and social wellbeing is also recognised. Against this backcloth, the Government has committed itself to meeting its election manifesto promises on improving health, tackling the root causes of ill health and social exclusion, and building strong families and communities. 'Well Into 2000' (DHSS, 1997) is seen by the Department of Health & Social Services as a new starting point for a sustained effort to tackle issues and problems of health and wellbeing.

The Vision

There are seven principles outlined in 'Well Into 2000' which will serve as signposts for future direction: social inclusion; social justice; healthy public policy; partnerships for health and wellbeing; healthy and supportive environments; strong, modern health and social services; meeting the challenge of change.

The Government states that this vision can only be effectively brought about by the working together of Government, national agencies, local agencies and communities. The recently-published document, 'Fit for the Future: A New Approach, (DHSS 1999), sets out proposals for restructuring health and social services over the next decade at least. Fit for the Future sets out seven key principles: equity; promoting health and wellbeing; quality; a local focus; partnership; efficiency; openness and accountability.

The Government is committed to the abolition of the internal market and to the improvement of services, with new organisational arrangements based on co-operation rather than competition. The number of Health Boards (four), Trusts (nineteen) and Health & Social Services agencies (five) will be reviewed. Such management arrangements for a population of 1.5 million are fragmented, too bureaucratic and the proposals are that these should change. However, structural differences will continue to create tension between the medical and social models of health, and increase the dominance of the medical model in the acute sector. Bywaters (1986) argues that medical expectations of patient passivity sit uneasily with the social work objectives of a self-empowered and self-directed clientele.

Another factor in this scenario is the newly-elected Northern Ireland Assembly, which will have strategic control of the HPSS and will take the final decision on its future structures.

The 'Fit for the Future' consultation document did not mention the term community development at all, in contrast to the high profile given to community development in the policy document 'Well Into 2000' (DHSS, 1997) which gave clear support to community development throughout. However, after extensive lobbying, Fit for the Future: A New Approach (DHSS, 1999) now makes reference to the importance of community development:

> *"Health and wellbeing is not the responsibility of HPSS alone. It requires the efforts of many others in the statutory, voluntary, community and private sectors. Individuals and local communities also have an important role to play.*
>
> *"The HPSS have to build partnerships with many different groups and, in keeping with the policies set out in Well Into 2000, adopt community development approaches to improving health and wellbeing. Any changes to their organisation and structures must therefore support, rather than hamper, co-operation with others."*

'Fit for the Future: A New Approach' makes several references to the community and voluntary sector on issues such as partnerships, and several of its guiding principles could connect with the community and voluntary sector and community development, however, these links are weak in the document.

Well Into 2000 states:

> *"The Board's (H&SS) plans will promote and employ community development approaches. Sound community development practices and principles underpin the Government's conviction that programmes should not be imposed from the top down, but should encourage voluntary action designed and developed within local communities... Community Development involves supporting local communities to identify the health and social concerns of greatest importance to them, and helping to devise and implement solutions. The Government wishes to see community development further extended, strengthened and promoted throughout Northern Ireland, and mainstreamed in all Health & Social Services agencies."*

The aim of achieving a community development approach and improved social justice will be emphasised by Health & Social Services and other agencies engaging more positively with local communities to tackle inequalities in health and wellbeing. This is an ambitious task, which will require a major rethink in how policies are created and delivered. It will necessitate movement from a service-led to a needs-led model of meeting needs, and will require the development and maintenance of partnerships between agencies and local people. In summary, a new culture needs to be built which:

- recognises the importance of the voluntary and community sectors in making a unique contribution to health and social wellbeing;
- improves inter-agency communication, co-operation and partnership working;
- strengthens the social fabric and support systems within communities, especially those facing multiple disadvantage;

One of the major ways of achieving the above is by creating a community development strategy which provides direct support to the community, so engendering a sense of local ownership and control.

If this is the situation contemporary community development faces, what can be learned from the past to ensure that opportunities can be grasped, and what are the more recent organisational issues which need to be understood? The rest of the Chapter seeks to address these questions.

Community Development in Northern Ireland Pre-1990s: Emergence and Decline

Caul and Herron (1992) report that voluntary and community activity in the fields of health and social welfare have a history stretching into the Nineteenth Century and beyond. Much of this activity was, similar to other countries in western Europe at that time, inspired by religious beliefs and/or a strong sense of civic duty. In Northern Ireland, many of the modern institutions and services in the welfare arena are descendants of such endeavours. Indeed, until the development in the late-1940s/early-1950s of a network of statutory social services - the county welfare authorities - the voluntary sector was the major provider of many services at a local level.

Community work, as a distinct method of social work, was first identified by the Younghusband Report (1959) which identified three strands of social work: case work, group work and community work. While in Britain it achieved pre-eminence and subsequently notoriety, in the community development projects of the late-1960s/early-1970s, in Northern Ireland, even with the restructuring of health and personal social services in the early-1970s (DHSS, 1972), it tended to remain a marginal activity in most areas. Nonetheless, there were a few notable exceptions, especially in the new town areas of Antrim, Craigavon and in the Greater Belfast area where community development was undertaken by a mixture of statutory and voluntary organisations. The Community Relations Commission employed a small number of Community Workers whose focus was increasingly on community development as a step towards community relations work.

The early-1970's also saw a significant growth in voluntary organisations. As Fraser (1980) described it:

> *"The early 1970s saw a tremendous growth in community activity and new, dynamic and progressive forms of voluntary effort in Northern Ireland. Pressures for social change came from a range of compassion for victims of misfortune, anger at injustices and fear of unrest. Thus, literally hundreds of*

local self-help community and pressure groups... emerged... some to try and meet immediate needs (eg lunch clubs, summer schemes, playgroups). At the other end of the scale, Government, motivated by a mixture of fear at social unrest and concern for the worst extremes of poverty and deprivation, backed community programmes (eg increased expenditure on community work, Belfast Areas of Need, etc). In the middle, lots of concerned and compassionate individuals became involved in organisations such as those running children's holiday schemes, helping the elderly and so on."

Overall, though, a number of factors contributed to the relegation of community development to the periphery of statutory social services. These included:

- The concentration on focusing on what the 1972 HPSS Order identified as 'persons in need', rather than taking a broader, community-based perspective.
- Budgetary constraints diverted resources from promotional/preventative activity such as community work, into more acute individual/family-focused activities.
- The 'democratic deficit', which has left Northern Ireland Government Departments relatively free from local influence and accountability, militated against more open and democratic methods of service delivery (such as community development).
- The tendency in government thinking, especially during the Thatcher era, to promote the notion of individual pathology and personal responsibility, again militated against more collective approaches to human problems and needs.
- The continued growth of a bureaucratic structure for delivering personal social services led Caul and Herron (1992) to bemoan: *"It is one of the very sad features of social work in Northern Ireland that ossified, complex organisations have been allowed to displace the original goals of professional social workers with a totally unjustifiable detachment from local communities."*

Against this rather bleak picture from the statutory sector, it was left largely to the voluntary sector to continue to work in local communities to develop and provide creative, imaginative services which met local needs. In many respects, such schemes challenged disadvantage, poverty and discrimination. They often promoted change and challenged statutory agencies. The Community Development Review Group (1991) have emphasised that this was occurring often in the most disadvantaged, ghettoised areas, and against a background of a troubled society, rife with sectarianism and often at the brink of civil war.

Sectarianism

Logue (1992) defines sectarianism in the following way:

> *"Sectarianism in the context of Northern Ireland is – discrimination arising from political or religious prejudice, leading to relationships of distrust between the two major political or religious communities. Sectarianism is not just a matter of economic, social or political consideration: nor is it simply a question of personal attitudes or behaviour. It is an historical and cultural phenomenon arising out of political and religious differences and perpetuated by group and self interest."*

Sectarianism in the Northern Ireland context is wider than religious differences. It has been used by Protestants and Catholics to defend or assert cultural and national identity and to promote social and economic advantage.

Brewer (1991) illustrates three levels of sectarianism, Ideas, individual action and social structure. He holds that Catholics and Protestants are both victims and perpetuators of discrimination and oppression at the ideological and interpersonal level, but states that Catholics are the major losers at the structural level. This is partly due to the institutionalisation of oppressive systems, structures, and stereotypes.

Sectarianism seems to have had a profound, but largely unacknowledged affect on health and social services in Northern Ireland. Health & Social Services staff are largely products of, and work within the divided society. Health & Social Staff and Managers are part of the problem but can be a part of the solution, by working in anti-sectarian/anti-oppressive ways. Health and Social Services agencies face a great challenge in actively developing and working towards an anti-sectarian and anti-oppressive agenda, and moving away from a non-sectarian approach and a cultural of denial and avoidance to an anti-sectarian approach.

Rediscovery

The 1990s have seen the 'rediscovery' of community development as what Craig (1995) identified "...*as a potential panacea...*" for political, social and economic dislocation, and as a vehicle through which greater dialogue can take place between agencies of the State and local communities. Much of the impetus for this, even in the Northern Ireland context, lies at both global and pan-European levels.

Policy statements and strategy documents issuing from major international bodies have supplemented and amplified a number of United Kingdom and local initiatives, culminating in the creation of a climate in which community development can begin to make a significant contribution to modern social welfare.

Figure 2 identifies a range of influences that have impacted to create an environment in Northern Ireland in which health and social welfare agencies are increasingly looking towards community development to make a contribution at a number of levels.

Figure 2: <u>**Significant Influences Impacting on Contemporary Community Development**</u>

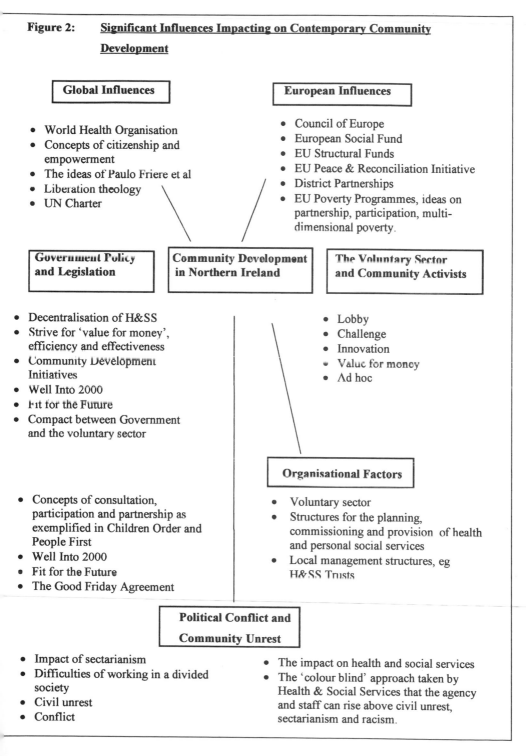

Global Influences

- World Health Organisation
- Concepts of citizenship and empowerment
- The ideas of Paulo Friere et al
- Liberation theology
- UN Charter

European Influences

- Council of Europe
- European Social Fund
- EU Structural Funds
- EU Peace & Reconciliation Initiative
- District Partnerships
- EU Poverty Programmes, ideas on partnership, participation, multi-dimensional poverty.

Government Policy and Legislation	Community Development in Northern Ireland	The Voluntary Sector and Community Activists

- Decentralisation of H&SS
- Strive for 'value for money', efficiency and effectiveness
- Community Development Initiatives
- Well Into 2000
- Fit for the Future
- Compact between Government and the voluntary sector

- Lobby
- Challenge
- Innovation
- Value for money
- Ad hoc

- Concepts of consultation, participation and partnership as exemplified in Children Order and People First
- Well Into 2000
- Fit for the Future
- The Good Friday Agreement

Organisational Factors

- Voluntary sector
- Structures for the planning, commissioning and provision of health and personal social services
- Local management structures, eg H&SS Trusts

Political Conflict and Community Unrest

- Impact of sectarianism
- Difficulties of working in a divided society
- Civil unrest
- Conflict

- The impact on health and social services
- The 'colour blind' approach taken by Health & Social Services that the agency and staff can rise above civil unrest, sectarianism and racism.

Global and European Influences

At a global level, the past two decades have seen increasing demands for social democracy, a process which Roche (1995) identifies as enabling ordinary citizens and local communities to play greater roles in the running of their affairs. Central to social democracy are the principles of empowerment and citizenship.

Writers such as Popple (1995) and O'Neill (1997), advocate that community work through processes of community development, community education and community planning can help promote these global principles and lead to social change. The World Health Organisation takes a similar view. In its strategy document 'Health For All 2000', (1986), a key principle advocated was the greater involvement of local communities in health and social services through the processes of communication, consultation and planning.

While such movements have been occurring on the world stage, a number of significant influences at European level have also promoted community development.

EU Third Poverty Programme and Brownlow Community Trust

The European Community developed anti-poverty programmes during the 1970s, 1980s and 1990s, which have been criticised for bureaucracy and small funding levels. However, these programmes marked a departure from market-based answers to difficult social and economic problems. In 1985, it was estimated that more than 51 million people in the EU had an income of below 50% of the average. (European Commission, 1991, Table A8, The Regions in the 1990s, Brussels.)

These programmes, while they failed to involve the EU in significant change, did raise the capacity of poverty research at a European level. In 1991, the Council of Ministers defined 'poverty' as the condition of: *"Persons whose resources material, cultural and social are so limited as to exclude them from the minimum acceptable way of life in the Member State in which they live."* (European Commission, 1991, ibid)

There was also a recognition that the impact of unemployment and lone parenthood had created a 'new poor', distinctive in many respects from those targeted by the traditional poverty programmes.

The EU Third Poverty Programme consisted of thirty-nine pilot projects, of which three were in Ireland, one in the North and two in the Republic. The central concepts were partnership, inter-agency strategies, multi-dimensional poverty, economic and social integration, additionality and participation. Brownlow, Craigavon, was chosen because of its unique experience of social exclusion and poverty. It was also selected because a group of community activists had come together and produced a report which echoed the broad headings of the Poverty Three concepts, 'The Greater Brownlow Review' (O'Neill and Heaney, 1988).

The EU Third Poverty Programme in Brownlow, Northern Ireland, was relatively successful (see Chapter 3). It created a structure for community participation and partnership; it also facilitated a range of projects, some of which are still very active. The Programme also made a strong contribution to EU and regional debate on tackling poverty. Limitations experienced included the absence of a significant economic partner and the feeling of powerlessness among some community activists. Statutory agencies, on the whole, did not follow the lead of Brownlow Community Trust in creating a strategic response to the poverty in the area. (Brownlow Community Trust: A Historical Account, Europe's Third Poverty Programme in Northern Ireland, 1989-1994, Gillespie, N.)

This process and the EU Special Initiative for Peace and Reconciliation has identified the need for action to combat social exclusion, which is a dynamic process affecting people experiencing poverty and disadvantage. There are still many vulnerable people being disadvantaged; disabled, long-term unemployed, victims, children and young people at risk, Travellers and ethnic minorities. Many of these groups are on the margins of society, and face multiple disadvantages and dislocation from the opportunities to participate fully in society.

Social inclusion involves looking beyond 'blaming the poor' for the problem, but rather examining and tackling the systems and structures that create disadvantage.

> *"Community development is an important change process which can address inclusion from the bottom up, embracing inclusion as both a means and an end. It is characterised by multi-dimensionality, partnership and*

participation. Community development addresses conflict and prejudice and can contribute to healing rifts, building trust and hence building peace."

(Social Inclusion Lessons from the Peace Programme,

Northern Ireland Voluntary Trust, 1999, Belfast)

At a policy level, Chanan (1992) reports that in 1989 the Council of Europe endorsed the importance of community work as a vehicle for change, while in the same year the European Foundation for the Improvement of Living and Working Conditions published findings which identified community action as a constructive response to people's living conditions (cited in Popple, 1995). A view from across Europe was emerging in the late-1980s/early-1990s that community work has a role to play in: assisting in the reconstruction of local economies and social systems; creating closer social and community cohesion and assisting in the invigoration of local communities.

The European Community through its Social Fund, the EU Poverty Programme, and additionally in the Northern Ireland context, the EU Special Initiative For Peace and Reconciliation Initiative, has directly supported a range of community development initiatives designed to promote the activities outlined above.

The Influences of Government Policy and Legislation

A range of government policies from the mid-1980s have promoted concepts of involvement, consultation and participation. This was happening against a backdrop which stressed 'value for money', efficiency and effectiveness. The latter constituted the pillars of an economic policy which created great financial pressures, with many local authorities and voluntary organisations experiencing diminishing budgets. In his critique of this period, Popple (1995), warns of the concern: *"... that community work could be used to offer low-cost strategies to tackle problems that demand substantial resources".* .

In 1993 the Voluntary Activity Unit (VAU) was established within the DHSS to maintain a focus within Government on voluntary activity. The VAU also has lead responsibility for volunteering and for community development. The Unit has had an important impact and has channelled EU structural funds and influenced other Departments in relation to community development and voluntary/statutory co-operation. The Regional Strategy for Health and

Social Wellbeing 1997-2002, published by DHSS in 1996, emphasises the importance of involving local people in the planning and ultimately the development of services. It recognised the significance of community development approaches to improving health and social wellbeing. Such directives are operationalised at a H&SS Board level by objectives being aimed at achieving a better understanding of local communities, in order to identify those most in need and determine the extent of need (SHSSB, 1995).

A number of recent social welfare legislative developments in Northern Ireland also impact on the potential for community development to play a more significant role in the planning, development, delivery and evaluation of social services. People First (1990) aimed at promoting the concept of community care. It has provided opportunities for community development to act particularly as a facilitator of local change and social inclusion. The Children Order (1995) similarly has opened up opportunities in engaging with local communities to meet the challenges posed by a broadened definition of 'children in need' and placing more emphasis on supporting families.

Targeting Health and Social Need

The Government has recently announced a New Targeting Social Need Initiative (New TSN, 1998) which aims to improve the social and economic conditions of disadvantaged people. Priorities for the next five years will be to: secure the involvement of local people in decisions about service provision through locally-sensitive purchasing; community development; involve agencies outside health and social services; develop the capacity to assess need for health and social care; evaluate the effectiveness of interventions; target resources and services where they are most needed; and encourage relevant research and development.

The authors would argue that one of the best ways of addressing New TSN is through a community development process, by which health and social services can engage meaningfully with disadvantaged people and listen to their concerns and problems, and work on these together to find potential solutions. This can be a challenge to professionals who consider themselves to be 'experts' in 'top down' solutions. It also uses a social, rather than a medical model of health.

Another problem is that some Health & Social Services Staff and Managers are using the language of community development, without having the benefit of proper training on community development values, principles and practice. The Policy to Practice Initiative, managed by the Community Development & Health Network, Northern Ireland, is highlighting some of these issues.

If New TSN is to be successful, Staff and Managers from the Health & Social Services should fully co-operate with each other, and with the voluntary and community sector. TSN initiatives should fully connect with community workers and projects in disadvantaged areas, in order to create a synergy and avoid potential duplication or misunderstanding.

The New TSN initiative is about identifying people in most need and attempting to ensure that government programmes are most effective in assisting them. It will cut across all Government Departments and beyond them, as poverty, ill health and disadvantage are multi-dimensional. However, it is possible to take a 'top down' approach to New TSN which neglects the opportunities provided by a community development strategy which encompasses inclusive 'top down and bottom up' approaches.

Across Northern Ireland a number of Health & Social Services Trusts have begun to see community development as a valuable contributor in operationalising current policies. This has complemented the continued efforts of the voluntary sector to promote, build up and harness community involvement in local health and social welfare projects.

It is also important to record a more critical perspective regarding such developments. The use of community development methods may be viewed as attempting to produce cheaper options in encouraging the growth of community- and/or voluntary-based alternative service providers. In a similar regard, engagement with communities concerning perceived needs set against a background of a constrained financial climate, may be seen as 'window dressing', rather than an exercise in consultation, partnership and participation.

As stated earlier in this Chapter, community development sits at the interface between statutory agencies and the communities they serve, and as at most interfaces, dilemmas, tensions and contradictions abound.

The following chapters will illustrate the importance of community development in developing real and meaningful dialogue and partnerships between statutory, voluntary and community sectors. The authors will demonstrate how community development has a legitimate and meaningful contribution to make to contemporary health and social services.

References

Baldock, P (1977) 'Why Community Action? The Historical Origins of the Radical Trend in British Community Work', Community Development Journal, 12 (3).

Brewer, J (1991) The Parallels Between Sectarianism and Racism. The Northern Ireland Experience in One Small Step Towards Racial Justice. The Teachings of Anti-Racism in DIPSW Programmes Improving Social Work Education and Training Eight CCETSW.

Bywaters (1986) 'Social Work and the Medical Profession, Arguments Against Unconditional Collaboration', British Journal of Social Work, 16 December No 6, p 670.

Caul, B and Herron, S (1992) A Service for People: Origins and Development of the Personal Social Services of Northern Ireland, December Publications, Belfast

Chanan, G (1992) Out of the Shadows: Local Community Action and the European Community, Final Report of the Research Project-Coping with Social and Economic Change at Neighbourhood Level, Office for Official Publications of the European Community, Luxembourg.

Community Development Review Group (1991) Community Development in Northern Ireland: Perspectives for the Future, CDRG, Belfast.

Couto, R A (1997) cited in 'Process-Focused, Product-Focused Community Planning . . .' by E Sadan and A Churchman in Community Development Journal, Volume 32, No 1, January.

Craig, G (1995) Foreword in K Popple, Analysing Community Work, Open University Press, Buckingham.

Department of Health & Social Services (1972) Health and Personal Social Services (Northern Ireland) Order, HMSO, Belfast.

Department of Health & Social Services (1990) 'People First' - Community Care in Northern Ireland, HMSO, Belfast.

Department of Health & Social Services (1991) Health and Personal Social Services (Northern Ireland) Order, HMSO, Belfast.

Department of Health & Social Services (1996) Monitoring and Evaluation of Community Development in Northern Ireland, DHSS, Belfast.

Department of Health & Social Services (1996) Health and Wellbeing: Into the Next Millennium, Regional Strategy for Health and Social Wellbeing 1997-2002, DHSS, Belfast.
* DHSS (1997) above report now 'Well Into 2000', DHSS, Belfast.

Department of Health & Social Services (1998) New Targeting Social Need, HMSO, Belfast.

Department of Health & Social Services (1999) Fit for the Future: A New Approach, DHSS, Belfast.

Department of Health & Social Services (1999) Targeting Health & Social Need, DHSS, Belfast.

Dominelli, L (1990) Women and Community Action, Venture Press, Birmingham.

Fraser, H (1980) Community Work in a Divided Society, Farset, Belfast.

Gough, I (1992) The Political Economy of the Welfare State, MacMillan, London.

Logue, K (1992) Anti Sectarianism and the Voluntary Community Sector Approach, Community Relations Council.

Naidoo, J and Wills, J (1994) Health Promotion Foundations for Practice, Balliere and Tindall, London.

Northern Ireland Voluntary Trust (1999) Social Inclusion Lessons from the Peace Programme, May, NIVT, Belfast.

O'Neill, M (1997) Towards a Participation Strategy Within Craigavon and Banbridge Community Health & Social Services Trust, Gilford.

O'Neill, M and Heaney, D (eds) (1988) The Greater Brownlow Review, Brownlow Community Development Association, Brownlow, Craigavon.

Popple, K (1995) Analysing Community Work: Its Theory and Practice, Open University Press, Buckingham.

Roche, M (1995) 'Citizenship and Modernity', review article in British Journal of Sociology, Vol 46, Issue No 4, December, London School of Economics.

Southern Health & Social Services Board (1995) Director of Social Services: Sixth Assessment of Need - 1995, Armagh, SHSSB.

Taylor, M and Presley, F (1987) Community Work in the United Kingdom 1982-1986, G Chanan (ed), Library Association Publication in association with Calouste Gulbenkian Foundation, London.

Traynor, C (1998) 'Social Work in a Divided Society' in Social Work and Social Change in Northern Ireland, Chapter 3, CCETSW, Belfast.

World Health Organisation (1986) Ottawa Charter from Health Promotion, Health for All 2000, WHO.

Younghusband, E L (1959) Report of the Working Party on Social Workers in the Local Authority Health & Welfare Services, HMSO, London.

2 Developing an Infrastructure to Support Community Development in Craigavon

Edwin Graham

Over the past five years an infrastructure has developed within the community and voluntary sector in Craigavon. This infrastructure plays a critical role in supporting community development and in supporting the community and voluntary sector generally. This Chapter examines the government policy and support that has enabled the development of the community infrastructure. It also highlights the need for an integrated strategy across all government departments to support community development and community participation.

Government Policy and Community Development

In 1993 the then Government published the document 'Strategy for the Support of the Voluntary Sector and for Community Development' (DHSS, 1993). The Strategy represented a significant milestone in terms of government policy in support of community development - it recognised the value of a community development approach and the independence of the voluntary sector.

In 1996 the Government published the 'Compact between Government and the Voluntary and Community Sector in Northern Ireland' (DHSS, 1998). The Compact was developed in collaboration with representatives from the voluntary sector. It builds on the significant achievements made since 1993 and is widely viewed as being a significant advance on the Strategy. These two documents are important as statements of central government policy in relation to the sector. However, there have been a host of other developments, which are reflected in a variety of documents indicating a changing relationship between the public and the voluntary sector.

In 1996 the Voluntary Activity Unit (VAU) in the Department of Health & Social Services commissioned a report on the 'Monitoring and Evaluation of Community Development in Northern Ireland' (DHSS, 1996). This report is particularly valuable for those organisations that have a networking or representative function. It clearly sets out a model of community development, focusing on individual and community empowerment.

The VAU document defines community development in the following way:

> *"Community development... is a way of working which is informed by certain principles which seek to encourage communities... to tackle for themselves the problems which they face and identify to be important, and which aim to empower them to change things by developing their own skills, knowledge and experience and also by working in partnership with other groups and with statutory agencies. The way in which such change is achieved is crucial and so both the task and the process are important."*

Part of the role of the VAU is to support community development across all government departments. However, the definition of 'community development' is variously understood in differing government departments.

The Department of the Environment (DOE) recently published its draft regional strategic framework, entitled 'Shaping our Future' (DOE, 1998). The document includes a page of *"Local community development guidelines for urban and rural areas."* The DOE's community development guidelines clearly reflect a different understanding of the term. The concept of empowerment is not evident: instead, the DOE focuses on more tangible outputs under the headings of *"...identity, vitality, proximity, accessibility, amenity and quality."*

The contrast between the DHSS and the DOE reflects the widely varying way in which the phrase 'community development' is used. Despite the fact that the VAU has a cross-departmental remit and that the VAU report clearly defines 'community development', there are few publications from Departments other than the DHSS that acknowledge the model of community development defined by the VAU.

Community development has a central role in the DHSS 1997-2002 Regional Strategy:

> *"Community development involves supporting local communities to identify the health and social concerns of greatest importance to them and helping them to devise and implement solutions. The Government wishes to see community development further extended, strengthened and promoted*

throughout Northern Ireland and mainstreamed in all health and social services agencies." (DHSS, 1997)

The Southern Health & Social Services Board (SHSSB) has responded to the regional strategy and to local lobbying, by incorporating a strategic objective of: *"...developing a strategic approach in community development"* (SHSSB, 1998).

Separate to the developments in health and social services, there has been major progress in relation to community participation in the context of sustainable development. In 1992, the United Nations held a Conference on Environment and Development in Rio de Janeiro (the Earth Summit). The result of the Earth Summit was Agenda 21 - an agenda for sustainable development in the 21st century.

> *"Agenda 21 addresses the pressing problems of today and also aims at preparing the world for the challenges of the next century... Its successful implementation is first and foremost the responsibility of governments... The broadest public participation and the active involvement of the non-governmental organisations and other groups should also be encouraged."*
>
> (United Nations, 1992)

The Agenda 21 report details specific ways in which public participation can be supported by governments. It also details ways in which the voluntary sector should be involved in the decision-making processes in relation to Agenda 21.

> *"Governments... should promote and allow the participation of non-governmental organisations in the conception, establishment and evaluation of official mechanisms and formal procedures designed to review the implementation of Agenda 21 at all levels."* (Ibid)

Five years after the Earth Summit there was little discernible action evident in Northern Ireland in relation to Agenda 21. However, Tony Blair, speaking as a newly appointed Prime Minister, stated that all local authorities in the UK should adopt local Agenda 21 strategies by the year 2000 (DETR, 1998). Subsequently, the Department of the Environment issued guidance on Agenda 21 to all district councils in Northern Ireland.

In the context of Agenda 21 the Department of the Environment, Transport and the Regions in England (DETR) has published a number of reports which provide guidance on community participation:

"We will... consider how to encourage public participation in decision-making. This is not just about getting agreement to decisions by local authorities and other public bodies, but involving local communities in identifying problems and opportunities, in the management of environmental assets such as public forests, and in taking action for change."

(DETR, 1998)

Similarly, the Local Government Management Board for England and Wales (LGMB) has published detailed guidance on community participation in relation to Agenda 21 (LMGB, 1993). There appears, however, to be a gap in this area in Northern Ireland. The DOE, in asking councils to implement Agenda 21 strategies, is encouraging them to participate in visioning exercises involving community participation, and is promoting the development of partnerships. However, the DOE does not appear to have produced any guidance for councils on how to develop community participation strategies, which may cause difficulties of interpretation for many councils.

In this context, it is interesting to consider how community participation and community development have been supported at a neighbourhood level.

Community Development in Craigavon

The Borough of Craigavon can be justly proud of a vibrant and dynamic community and voluntary sector. Outside of Belfast and Derry, it probably has the best-developed community and voluntary sector of any local government district in Northern Ireland. Since the formation of Craigavon as a local government district in 1973, there has been substantial support by statutory agencies for community development in the district. Part of the reason why such support was targeted at Craigavon was because of the historical context that led to the development of a 'new town'. It was obvious that there was a need to create a community where none had existed previously.

The Borough Council and the Health Trust provided substantial support for community development through the 1980s and 1990s. Craigavon Borough Council, like the other twenty-five councils in Northern Ireland, was funded to provide community services, but there was never any departmental policy that clearly articulated the purpose of community services provision. The result is a sporadic response across Northern Ireland. Craigavon is one of the better areas where support was provided.

Craigavon Borough Council has a Principal Community Services Officer and Community Services Officers in Lurgan and central Craigavon (with a vacant post in Portadown). In addition, it has fourteen community centres. Each community centre has a Centre Manager who has responsibility for community development in their area. Craigavon Borough Council disperses small grants totalling approximately £80,000 per annum, and also has a Community Relations Officer with a grants programme of £20,000 per annum.

The Craigavon and Banbridge Community Health & Social Services Trust (CBCHSST) has a variety of staff with responsibility for supporting community development in one form or another. What is unusual about the Craigavon and Banbridge Trust is that it retained a Community Work Team at a time when all other health trusts in Northern Ireland saw little importance in community development, and certainly did not retain staff with a primary community development focus (see Chapter 4). In this context, with such a range of support coming from two key statutory agencies, a wide variety of community groups and voluntary organisations began to develop.

In 1989 the European Poverty Three Programme funded the development of Brownlow Community Trust (BCT) in the central area of Craigavon. BCT has subsequently developed to become Moylinn House Community Development Support Services Agency. The evaluation of BCT recognised that:

> *"It created a structure of participation for community actors which offered an important arena for engagement with statutory agencies", and, "it made a distinctive contribution to the debate... about how statutory and voluntary agencies could build partnerships..."*

> (Gaffikin and Morrissey, 1994)

BCT's experience laid foundations for the establishment of a range of partnerships between voluntary organisations in Craigavon and statutory agencies.

In addition to the support from local statutory agencies, funding also became available from European Structural Funds, the European Peace Programme and the National Lottery Charities Board as well as other funders. The local statutory funders provided the matching funding which was required to enable local groups to access significant funds from Europe. In this way, the Health Trust and the Council entered into a variety of working relationships with local groups.

In 1994 the European Structural Funds created a new measure entitled the 'community infrastructure measure'. This measure was important in providing funding for community infrastructure projects, but it was probably more important for the way in which it established the concept of community infrastructure.

The result of the funding that flowed from a variety of sources was a strategic network of representative voluntary organisations that cover Lurgan, Portadown and the rural areas. The principal organisations in this network are the representative umbrella organisations: Community Network Portadown (CNP), Lurgan Council for Voluntary Action (LCVA) and the Tyrone, Antrim, Down, Armagh sub-regional rural network (TADA). These organisations link directly with statutory agencies through Moylinn House Community Development Support Services Agency. The four organisations – Moylinn House, LCVA, CNP and TADA, work closely together. They collaborate on a number of projects as well as being involved in a variety of work specific to their own area.

The strength of the network lies in the diversity that is inherent in its membership. Each of the four organisations has a different structure and each approaches the task of supporting community development in a different, though complementary manner. In this way there is a synergy from the combined actions of the organisations, although, at the same time, each organisation jealously protects its independence. The co-ordination between the voluntary organisations on the ground did not happen because statutory agencies decided that it should - rather it happened because voluntary organisations identified benefits to their own individual organisation from being part of a wider network.

27

Community Infrastructure in Craigavon

The experience of LCVA demonstrates an approach to the development of community infrastructure and it provides an example of the benefits which can be derived from such an approach.

In the initial years of LCVA's existence, the focus of development was on the creation of opportunities for networking. In 1995, there was little contact between many developing community groups and voluntary organisations in the Lurgan area. It was obviously apparent that there were benefits to be gained from collaboration between a range of different voluntary organisations and groups. LCVA's initial energies were committed to building networks and collaborations and these energies soon bore fruit. In a short space of time many opportunities were developed to bring organisations together to discuss a range of common issues such as transport, childcare and community relations.

It soon became apparent that there were significant benefits to be gained from developing initiatives that engaged statutory and voluntary agencies working together to address needs in a holistic way. LCVA strategically focused on a range of specific issues in an attempt to address social exclusion and to create opportunities for community empowerment.

Over the past three years, energy has been focused on supporting a spread of organisations. The following list gives an idea of the types of organisations that have developed as a result.

Aghagallon/Aghalee Partnership

LCVA provided support for the local community groups in Aghalee and Aghagallon. Benefits were identified from the joint collaboration between the two Committees in Aghalee and Aghagallon - most notably community relations benefits, since Aghalee was perceived as being Protestant and Aghagallon was perceived as being Catholic. LCVA supported the development of the Aghagallon/Aghalee Partnership to address the community relations issues, and also to provide a broader base on which projects could develop. This project received funding from the Craigavon District Partnership to employ a Development Worker, and with her commitment much progress has been achieved and local projects are developing, such as a community arts project, a rambling club, a youth forum, adult education classes, a newsletter and committee training.

Craigavon Health Information Project (CHIP)

The Craigavon Health Information Project is a partnership between a number of voluntary organisations and statutory agencies. The purpose of CHIP is to promote health information in disadvantaged communities, and it uses a number of volunteers to achieve this purpose. Two members of staff are employed to co-ordinate and provide support and training for the volunteers.

CHIP was initially funded by the Health Trust and by Peace and Reconciliation money through both NIVT and the District Partnership. It has recently undertaken an evaluation, and as a result the Southern Health & Social Services Board is likely to provide continued funding for the project whenever the Peace and Reconciliation Funding expires.

Craigavon and Banbridge Community Transport Project

LCVA was concerned about the proliferation of mini-buses in many small community groups, and at the same time identified a lack of services, particularly for people with disabilities. In response to this identified need, LCVA commissioned a major piece of research by the University of Ulster to identify the need for new transport provision in the Craigavon and Banbridge area, and to recommend ways of addressing that need. As a result of this initiative, the Craigavon and Banbridge Community Transport Project was formed.

The Community Transport Project is a partnership of a wide range of organisations, and it has been very successful in influencing the development of transport policies in the Craigavon and Banbridge area.

Recently, Ulsterbus have announced two new routes which they have created in the Aghagallon/Aghalee area and in the Blackskull area in response to the need identified by the Community Transport Project. A host of other initiatives are currently being planned.

Lurgan Community Relations Project

From the outset LCVA had been involved in a range of discussions which impacted on community relations in the area. There was an obvious need for a worker, dedicated to community relations, to create opportunities for community relations training and to provide linkages between the different projects which were impacting on community relations across the Lurgan area.

LCVA worked in partnership with Lurgan Community Trust and Shankill Community Projects to develop the Lurgan Community Relations Project. The Community Relations Council from the outset actively supported the project. With their funding, it has been possible to appoint a worker to support the development of this project.

Craigavon and Banbridge Artscare

Artscare is an initiative within the Health & Social Services to provide opportunities for people in healthcare settings to participate in the arts. LCVA engaged with Craigavon and Banbridge Artscare to widen out the provision to ensure that people in community settings could benefit as much as people in health service settings. LCVA also worked with the Artscare Committee to develop a programme which was creating opportunities for the development of community relations, and raising awareness of the wide spread of differing cultural traditions in our society.

This programme has been hugely successful, with a host of small events being held throughout the Craigavon and Banbridge areas. It has received praise from local media and entertainment people such as Paul Clark and Gene Fitzpatick when they have participated in Artscare activities, as well as from the Northern Ireland Artscare Committee and the Health Trust.

The Craigavon and Banbridge Artscare group has provided great benefits for people in the community and in health service settings. The group has received a small grant from the District Partnership to support the Cultural Traditions Programme: however, most of the resources that the project has used have come from within existing statutory and voluntary organisations particularly within the Health Service.

Craigavon and Banbridge Volunteer Bureau

Craigavon and Banbridge Volunteer Bureau plays a critical role in providing support for volunteers in the Craigavon area. LCVA has provided substantial support to the Volunteer Bureau and is represented on the Bureau's Management Committee. Chapter 10 describes its work with supported volunteers

Services to Support the Community and Voluntary Sector

In addition to the specific organisations named above, LCVA provides substantial support to a host of community groups and voluntary organisations – most of them in the Lurgan area. Examples of these services include a payroll advice service, clerical support, desktop publishing, graphics design, a recruitment administration service, and a monthly mailing to all affiliated groups. LCVA publishes an annual Directory of Affiliated Organisations to provide a resource to LCVA member organisations, statutory agencies and private interest groups. Constitutions are created by LCVA and tailored to the individual needs of community organisations. LCVA has produced an associated publication - Model Constitutions for Community Groups and Voluntary Organisations, to provide guidance in this area. LCVA also provides fax, e-mail and internet access for affiliated groups, as well as a venue for meetings.

Building Relationships With the Statutory Sector

Parallel to the development of projects and services identified above, LCVA has committed energy to the development of relationships with the statutory sector. From the outset, the Health Trust recognised the benefits to be gained from developing such relationships across a range of activities.

In 1996, the announcement of the Special Support Programme for Peace and Reconciliation opened up new opportunities for LCVA. The organisation took a lead role in supporting the development of the Craigavon District Partnership, and in providing support and training for the voluntary sector members who were appointed to that Partnership.

In 1997, LCVA worked alongside the Community Work Team in the Health Trust to organise a conference to highlight the disparity between the priority for community development in the DHSS Regional Strategy, and the stated objectives in the SHSSB's Draft Purchasing Prospectus. As a result of this conference and the campaign that was associated with it, the SHSSB revised its Final Purchasing Prospectus to include a section on community development.

More recently LCVA has been building links with Craigavon Borough Council through its newly-appointed Sustainability Officer. LCVA has been working alongside the Council to support the development of community participation in relation to the Council's work on sustainable development and visioning.

Four conclusions can be drawn from the history of community development in Craigavon: international policy supports community development and community participation; the international policy is reflected in some departmental policy in Northern Ireland; for a variety of reasons, the community development practice in the Borough of Craigavon has been very good, resulting in a strategic network of umbrella organisations as well as a host of varied groups and organisations; the value of the sector has been internationally recognised for its contribution to social cohesion, and its ability to target social exclusion. The other, less positive conclusion that must be drawn is that there are contradictions between different government departments in their understanding of 'community development'.

From the perspective of the DHSS, there are clear benefits in terms of health and social gain to be derived from incorporating a community development approach and providing opportunities for community participation. Such benefits have been well articulated in international documents, as well as in the DHSS's own publications.

From the perspective of the DOE, there are also clear benefits to be derived by developing a community development approach and providing opportunities for community participation. Again, such benefits are clearly articulated in documents from the Local Government Management Board.

What is missing is an integrated strategy for community development and community participation. It appears that the current strategies to support community development and community participation are being primarily driven by international developments. As these international initiatives filter down, they are compartmentalised into departmental policies. In the apparent absence of an attempt at an inter-departmental level to integrate these policies, the result tends to be disjointed actions and conflicting approaches at the local level.

From the perspective of a local voluntary organisation with the role of supporting community development and community participation, government support appears fragmented. It seems obvious that there would be benefits to be gained from having a joined-up approach to support community development and community participation.

The Role of the Community and Voluntary Sector in Northern Ireland

The value of the community and voluntary sector in Northern Ireland over the past thirty years has been widely recognised: *"The voluntary sector has significantly contributed to holding society together."* (European Commission, 1995)

And, in terms of social exclusion the voluntary sector has also an important role:

> *"Much of the existing expertise in combating social exclusion lies outside the public domain... the full involvement of non-governmental bodies and local*

*and community groups (including youth services and women's groups) would
be a prerequisite for success... in the Social Inclusion priority."*

(European Commission, 1995)

Writing about the need for the community and voluntary sector to be involved in the delivery
of the Peace Programme, Hugh Frazer identified the importance of a community
infrastructure:

*"When people become objects of the process of regeneration and are not
active participants in their own liberation, then local development is not
addressing the issue of social exclusion... Empowering the community as a
whole to develop the necessary infrastructure of local organisations... is
essential."*

(Frazer, 1995)

Developments on the horizon suggest exciting times ahead for community development in
Craigavon. Remarkable achievements have been made to date in the context of relatively
little policy direction from government. This situation is set to improve:

- The DOE's recent consultation exercise on the Regional Strategic Framework created
  opportunities for community involvement hitherto unknown in that Department. The
  report of that consultation identified the need for community development. It is
  reasonable to expect that this process will continue, and that the DOE will incorporate the
  VAU definition of 'community development' and the model set forth by the VAU in
  1996.

- The current review of the provision of community services in district councils is expected
  to highlight the absence of a departmental policy for community service provision,
  providing opportunities for a significant policy gap to be filled.

- The creation of new government departments provides opportunities for the achievements
  of the VAU to be buttressed, and for new sets of relationships to be formed across
  departments, to provide opportunities for further promoting community development.

- The development of Local Agenda 21 strategies in district councils will necessitate community participation strategies. As these develop locally, it is expected that they will impact on the DOE, adding further impetus to the drive for coherent community development and community participation policies and strategies.

- The development of a support document for the voluntary sector Compact, will provide opportunities to explore ways in which cross-departmental strategies can be developed.

- The creation of the Civic Forum will open up opportunities for community participation and cross-sectoral working at a level never before experienced in Northern Ireland.

- A 'Policy to Practice' initiative is being undertaken by the Community Development & Health Network in collaboration with Craigavon and Banbridge Community Health & Social Services Trust and four other Trusts. This will provide opportunities for the Trust to reaffirm its commitment to community development, and to develop an adequate policy framework for this important area of its work.

- Craigavon Borough Council's work on Local Agenda 21 and its visioning exercise will provide major opportunities for community participation. It is hoped that as a result of these two major initiatives, a coherent local strategy to support community participation could be developed.

The community infrastructure built up in Craigavon over the last few years should ensure that these developments reach community and voluntary groups operating at all levels throughout the area.

References

Craigavon Borough Council (1994) Community Services Policy Document, CBC.

Department of the Environment (1998) Shaping our Future, DOE.

Department of the Environment, Transport and the Regions (1998), Opportunities for Change, DETR.

Department of the Environment, Transport and the Regions (1998) Sustainable Local Communities for the 21st Century, DETR.

Department of Health & Social Services (1993) Strategy for the Support of the Voluntary Sector, DHSS, Belfast.

Department of Health & Social Services (1996) Monitoring and Evaluation of Community Development in Northern Ireland, DHSS, Belfast.

Department of Health & Social Services (1997) Well Into 2000, DHSS, Belfast.

Department of Health & Social Services (1998) Compact between Government and the Community and Voluntary Sector in Northern Ireland, DHSS, Belfast.

European Commission (1995) Implementing Europe's Programme for Peace, EC.

European Commission (1995) Guidance for the Social Inclusion Priority of the Special Support Programme for Peace and Reconciliation, EC.

Frazer, H (1995) The Importance of Community Involvement in Integrated Local Development Initiatives, NICVA, Belfast.

Gaffikin, F and Morrissey, M (1994) Brownlow Community Trust, Evaluation Report, BCT.

Local Government Management Board (1993), Community Participation in Local Agenda 21, LGMB.

Southern Health & Social Services Board (1996) Final Purchasing Prospectus 1996/7-1998/9, SHSSB.

Southern Health & Social Services Board (1998) Final Purchasing Prospectus 1997/8-1999/2000, SHSSB.

United Nations (1992) Report of the United Nations Conference on Environment and Development, United Nations.

3   The Poverty Three Experience In Craigavon - The Role of Community Development and Education in Partnership and Participation

Dr Norman Gillespie

Introduction

This chapter will focus on the relationship between community development and community education, and the part that both these processes play in addressing the issues of poverty and powerlessness. In order to demonstrate this, it will draw on the experience of the Third European Anti-Poverty Programme (Poverty Three) in Brownlow, Craigavon (Brownlow Community Trust) which operated from 1989 to 1994. The community development process has often been adopted by area-based programmes and it was a central strategy in the Brownlow project, although Poverty Three was not a community development programme per se. Community education, it will be argued, is very much a crucial component for not only the successful implementation of community development projects, but is a central concern for any programmes designed to address the problems of social exclusion and powerlessness. More importantly, perhaps, it is becoming increasingly recognised that it is central to the whole debate about promoting participatory democracy and citizenship, which is central to contemporary issues in social policy and practice. In this sense, it is important that both community development and education strategies work in harness with each other, and it is the nature of this dual approach that often decides the relative success, or failure, of area-based programmes designed to promote partnership and participation. This process will, therefore, form a central focus of this Chapter in order to contribute to a better understanding of the complexities, difficulties and opportunities presented by such an approach, and its implications on a wider scale.

Partnership and Participation

The principles of partnership and participation were two of the primary guiding principles of the Poverty Three Programme. The promotion of these principles can highlight some of the ways in which new approaches in community and adult education can make a significant contribution to the community development process and the promotion of empowerment. Indeed, these were issues which frequently arose in relation to the Poverty Three Programme in Brownlow, and this in turn was to highlight the need for such a system of education in order to effectively address social exclusion and marginalisation. While recognising its strengths, however, it is also important to stress the limitations of community development. Many of the constraints on community development in local and regional settings are imposed from outside the local and regional community, sometimes by the national and, increasingly, by the international community. Environmental degradation, pollution and contamination, and international economic arrangements, are all areas of activity which have a major effect quantitatively and qualitatively on human life. And they are all areas in which decision-making is restricted, and even the power to influence is limited.

In these circumstances, it is well to bear in mind that the provision of opportunities for a community to participate in its own development at the local or regional level carries no automatic progression towards, or guarantee of, provision to participate at other levels. In fact, a cynical or authoritarian government could well provide opportunities for community development at the local level as a diversion or a safety valve. To fashion modes of participation which bring these decisions under effective community influence, let alone community control, is at present unlikely to be realised. This point was made in the early American anti-poverty programmes, such as in the assertion that the so-called 'War on Poverty' flew in the face of the very nature of American society. It was re-emphasised in the Community Development Project in Great Britain the following decade, which put down analyses of urban deprivation as an inevitable consequence of the working of international capital, and the resultant inherent inequalities expressed in such terms as high unemployment, low income and benefits and poor housing. Indeed, by raising expectations and then failing to deliver, such programmes may even have an overall negative or zero net impact, at least in terms of community morale. The Poverty Three Programme, which went beyond the traditional community development approach, faced similar difficulties in that some local representatives expected the Programme to redress problems that would have required substantial shifts in national policy on issues such as public expenditure and welfare benefits.

However, the increasing emphasis, emanating from the European Union, on integrated approaches to community regeneration and on forming effective partnerships between local people, voluntary organisations and government departments and agencies, offers community development an opportunity to counteract the increasing co-option that was taking place in the community movement (Lovett et al, 1994). People in local communities have been well ahead of the EU and their local political representatives in recognising the essential links between social, economic, health and environmental issues affecting their everyday lives. They have campaigned for years for such co-ordination; for decentralisation and flexibility; and for real participation in the decision-making process. They have had to struggle against the bureaucratic, uninformed and often unresponsive nature of government agencies and departments.

That situation has been undergoing slow but considerable change in recent years as large voluntary organisations, statutory bodies, government departments and agencies have become involved in local community regeneration. It has, however, been pointed out (Lovett, et al, 1994) that those concerned in this process have little or no knowledge of community development principles and practices, and that they often have their own, conflicting, agendas. The Poverty Three Programme was, however, concerned with exploring the issues and problems arising out of attempts to construct such partnerships between local activists and government agencies; between community development and community enterprise. It is argued here that the relative success of such programmes depends on the form and extent of the educational and training element contained in the whole process of initiating, developing, and establishing working partnerships. In this sense, it is therefore crucial that adequate resources and time are allocated, in order to provide the necessary training and education required. If empowerment is the extent to which people can be involved in decisions about themselves, their community and the various groups to which they belong, community development and community education are the twin processes that enable this to occur.

Community Development and Education

There has been substantial debate over the past thirty years or so on the nature of community development and the role of education in this process. While the extent of community development work in the UK and Ireland has expanded considerably since the early 1970s its form has changed considerably. The experience of community development in the past illustrated one of the fundamental dilemmas of social change, in that elected political representatives viewed attempts at extending popular participation in the decision-making process as a threat to the 'democratic process' (that is, their own position). Such views were based upon uncontested assumptions about popular control and democracy. In the 'empowerment culture' of the present, the democratic process needs to be extended to ensure that marginalised and socially-excluded sections of the population, as well as everyone else, can influence decisions on a day to day basis. It is no longer widely accepted that democracy is simply about electing particular individuals (in Northern Ireland usually on constitutional and/or law and order issues), who then make all the relevant decisions and representations for their 'constituents', every four or five years. Indeed, Northern Ireland has been a classic example of how such a narrow interpretation creates and intensifies powerlessness and all its negative connotations. It is now claimed that community development, when harnessed to integrated strategies concerned with popular planning and decision-making, ensures that the democratic process operates more effectively and efficiently in tackling the multi-faceted problems of disadvantaged communities. This has been one of the assumptions underpinning the more recent work of some of the agencies and organisations engaged in community development work and community education in Northern Ireland.

If we look specifically to the role of education in this process, we should consider the present prevalent model of community education which involves a synthesis of community work and community development, with an emphasis on new structures for community and social organisations. It involves community education acting to provide locally-based information, advice and resources on the one hand, and facilitating learning relevant to social action on the other. Accepting the nature of the pluralist society, it is concerned with improving understanding and communication between conflicting groups, and promoting co-operation between statutory agencies, and between statutory agencies and the community. It seeks to alleviate the problems faced by communities by focusing on integrated responses designed to maximise synergy. Its focus is to a large extent concerned with developing partnership models of organisation, and facilitating user/community participation in social and economic regeneration programmes. While very much in the ascendancy, it still fails to adequately address the issue of resolving problems at a local level that are a consequence of wider macro-economic factors. Despite this constraint, however, the Brownlow experience provided an opportunity to consider the feasibility of incorporating such a model in initiatives designed to alleviate the worst aspects of poverty in communities undergoing widespread and multiple forms of disadvantage.

The Brownlow project demonstrated that a comprehensive model of community education needs to embrace a number of principles concerned with its relevance to knowledge (and control of it) and how that knowledge can affect the power relations of society at a community level. It follows that such knowledge needs to have a close relationship with practice that includes the community development process. This model would not only benefit this process, but facilitate the wider aims and objectives of ambitious anti-poverty programmes such as Poverty Three, that are designed to address powerlessness and promote realistic social and economic regeneration strategies.

Brownlow Community Trust (BCT) underlined the need for community development to play a central role in the process of facilitating community education and vice versa. This is an essential ingredient in promoting an overall strategy of enabling communities to address the problems associated with social and economic exclusion. Community education seeks to enable people to become producers of change rather than consumers, agents rather than recipients Community development seeks to provide an arena where this production by people of economic, social or cultural change is in close collaboration with public and professional agencies, rather than remote from or antagonistic to them. The underlying beliefs of community development are that there is a need for people to become the producers and agents of development in their communities, and that they can learn to be such. It has been claimed that the most practical vehicle for achieving this in the contemporary sense, is through forging partnerships between communities, and between the various agencies and organisations involved in this type of work. This should ensure an optimisation of activity and impact through pursuing complementary (though multiple) strategies, avoiding duplication and ensuring an absence of competing interests for scarce resources.

Community education can facilitate this process through providing appropriate education and training for those involved in the partnership, as well as the community in general. However, this needs to be done within the context of the wider social forces that shape and influence the conditions and experiences of the individuals concerned, and within the philosophy and practice of community development If the latter is seen as an essential foundation for improving social and economic conditions (because of its inherent principles concerning justice, participation and empowerment), then these principles need to be articulated and discussed by those involved in such programmes.

The debate on the role of community education in community development has been forwarded by developments in community work in general and changes in social policy. As one influential report noted (contemporaneously with the establishment of the Poverty

Programme in Brownlow), *"Community education and learning are integral to community development: without these there can be no movement, no progress, even no development."* (Community Development Review Group, 1991).

Community Practice and Participation

Writing about participation within the 'Community Support Programme', McShane (1993) describes community participation in policy development and service delivery as being on a continuum which ranges from 'information' to 'consultation' to 'participation/partnership'. She cites 'information' as the first, vital step towards participation, and stresses the importance of it being presented in clear language that people understand. 'Consultation', the next aspect of the continuum, requires those holding power for policy development or service provision to enter into consultation with local people or service users, to hear their views on existing policies, services or plans for the future. She reiterates that *"this should be an open process promoting the development of mutual trust and not just a token exercise."* (McShane, 1993). The third step on the continuum is 'participation', meaning an active input from service users and local people on what type of policies or services should be formulated, and how. McShane (1993) identifies participation to be a dynamic process, involving people in having an opportunity to participate at different levels and forms as they freely decide to, in accordance with their levels of confidence, and appropriate to their needs and choices. The practical complexities, tensions and opportunities presented by this position and other models of participation, as well as the implications for other developments in community practice, will be considered in relation to the Poverty Three experience in a later section of this Chapter.

Recent community practice has been deployed to support developing policies for community care, voluntary initiative and self-help. These all pre-date 1979, but are very much a hallmark of the Conservative administration with its emphasis on extending the scope of market forces, or rebalancing the contribution of non-commercial provision in favour of voluntary/community sector involvement.

This was a response to changing demographic patterns, reductions in working hours and increasing unemployment (for a detailed analysis of these trends and their implications for Northern Ireland see Gaffikin and Morrissey, 1990). It also led to a greater emphasis on co-operation between agencies and professionals, the development of multidimensional approaches to social and economic problems, and the promotion of pluralism through partnerships and participation. Community education and community development have a crucial role in this respect, with the implications of both of these for empowerment, citizenship and democracy. The next section will consider the specific experience of the Poverty Three Programme in Northern Ireland, which was essentially a 'model action' project designed to address these issues.

The Experience of Brownlow Community Trust

This section presents a brief account of the Third European Anti-Poverty Programme in Northern Ireland.[1] The recipient of support under the programme - Brownlow Community Trust, in Craigavon, was one of three 'model action' projects in the UK, which each received approximately £1million (which was 'matched' by other sources, mainly statutory) from the European Commission between 1989 and 1994, to develop innovative strategies and projects with marginalised and socially-excluded sections of the population. Each project was to be guided by a number of principles of which the primary ones were partnership, participation and multidimensionallty.

The 'new city' of Craigavon was originally planned to consist of the established towns of Lurgan and Portadown, their hinterlands and a newly-developed centre between the two (of which Brownlow was to be the main housing sector). Lurgan and Portadown, however, although subsequently included in the Craigavon Borough Council area, never identified with the Craigavon concept, which became synonymous (in local terminology at least) with Brownlow and the new 'central' area - which was never completed.

The first crucial step in the development of Brownlow Community Trust (BCT) was the publication of the Greater Brownlow Review (GBR) in 1988, as a result of the efforts of local activists and concerned statutory representatives. The GBR concluded that, while many of the problems highlighted in the document were a consequence of the position of Northern Ireland as the second poorest region within the EEC, there were particular problems in relation to Brownlow that needed to be emphasised. It added that the feeling of isolation and alienation prevalent in the area, could only be 'overcome' through a partnership between the

---

[1] For a complete account see Gillespie (1994)

local people and statutory organisations. The GBR led to the development of the Brownlow Community Development Association (BCDA) and the appointment by the DOE of a Consultant to report on economic regeneration opportunities in Brownlow (The Brownlow Initiative). BCDA went on to produce Brownlow 2000 (March 1989), which was a document designed as a focal point for organisations and interest groups concerned with working for the regeneration of Brownlow. Discussions on the issues raised in this document led to the Brownlow Review Update in June 1989, which underlined the need to promote greater co-ordination and integration between the various statutory agencies concerned, and also between the agencies and the community. By September 1989 it became apparent that the Programme could qualify for funding under the EC's Third Anti-Poverty Programme, given the relevance of the proposals contained in Brownlow 2000 to the Programme's stipulations. An application was hurriedly prepared with the help of the Consultant, and the requirement for a partnership between statutory and voluntary/community organisations accelerated and transformed the process of co-operation, which led to the formation of BCT as an umbrella group to formally make the application.

Following the success of the application, the main actors embarked upon the work of defining the form and extent of poverty in the community, and establishing the means for addressing it. After a period of intensive debate and definition, a number of groups were identified as those most in need of targeting by the Programme. These were women/single parents, young and long-term unemployed, and children. It was also agreed that there should be an over-riding health theme. This definitional phase was the first of five contractual periods. These were designed to meet specific guiding principles in the development of each project, under the co-ordination of a Central Unit in Lille.

The second contractual period (July 1990-June 1991) saw the establishment of BCT as a functioning project, with the appointment of a number of key staff to develop work with the targeted groups. Following the appointment of a Director and Information/Publicity Officer came the appointments of Health Project Worker, Women's Project Worker and Unemployed Project Worker. The Board of Management/Directors was chaired by the Director of the Craigavon and Banbridge Unit of Management of the Southern Health & Social Services Board. In addition to initiating a number of projects and establishing forums for consultation with local people, the Trust began to receive a rising number of requests for grant aid from a wide representation of groups.

The role of the Health Worker was essentially concerned with promoting a social model of health development that would encompass a holistic approach. The Women's Project Worker was responsible for a number of related themes from encouraging the growth and development of a wide range of general women's interest groups, to particular issue-oriented ones.

The Unemployed Project Worker's post had essentially two main focuses of concern. Firstly, it was to ensure that existing and planned initiatives for unemployed people were developed in a co-ordinated manner as part of an overall strategy. Secondly, they were to develop work with young unemployed people in particular (though not exclusively) in a 'creative' way. All three project workers were to work closely together, as there were large areas of mutual interest and concern. Together with the Information/Publicity Worker they were to ensure that the Trust developed and maintained a high level of interest in, and knowledge of its work. This was crucial in order to fulfil the level of visibility and participation required by the Poverty Three Programme. To help further this aim, the first copy of the BCT Newsletter Brownlow Matters was launched (December 1990). This included articles on the work of BCT, its role, staff and services available. It was delivered free to every household in Brownlow. By the time it reached its full complement in 1992, the Board consisted of ten statutory Directors (including the Chair), thirteen local community Directors and one Representative from Northern Ireland Voluntary Trust.

Throughout the development of the project, BCT was ideally placed to be used as a model for developing models of participation and partnership, in a multidimensional framework, due to the principles of Poverty Three coinciding with attempts by the lead statutory agency on the Board (SHSSB) to develop such principles in response to a number of government recommendations. The work of the Trust, however, also needs to be placed within the wider context of decreasing living standards generally for the worst-off sections of the population (which were being felt at least as much in Brownlow as elsewhere).

This included increasing unemployment and decreases in the real value of key benefits. Such factors were acting to increase poverty and social exclusion, at a time when BCT was attempting to reduce it at a local level. However, by the end of the project the Trust had targeted a number of areas which were being addressed through developing projects designed to implement the key elements of its strategy.

The unemployed project included work on enhancing opportunities for local people to compete on an equal basis with the job market through the provision of accessible childcare facilities. Activities designed to develop a sense of positive identity for Brownlow also received ongoing attention. Developments which the Worker was engaged in included:

- Tullygally 18+ Group: A self-help programme of personal skill development with ongoing and long-term unemployed people.

- Drumgor Unemployed Group: A programme of social and personal development was facilitated by the Worker.

- Edenbeg Unemployed Group: A programme of self-empowerment, involving community education, arts and practical activities, with access to essential childcare.

- Craigavon Unemployed Workers Centre (CUWC): Support was given for strategies to develop its resources for quality training. The centre also received substantial grant-aid from BCT which allowed it to develop its campaigning work, training and mobile crèche facilities.

- Cultural Activities: The Trust helped establish and develop a community arts group as a vehicle for local people to develop skills, self-confidence and esteem.

- Craigavon Leisure Centre Pilot Scheme: The Trust developed this initiative aimed at facilitating access to low-cost recreational facilities.

- Challenging Debt: BCT supported an inter-agency group which initiated a pilot loan scheme through the Credit Union (itself supported initially by the Trust), to assist Brownlow residents in debt or seeking access to loans for essential items.

- Historical/Environmental Projects: This included the restoration of one of the oldest Quaker graveyards in Ireland, using local unemployed people.

- Brownlow Stream Video: BCT and CUWC produced this video to highlight problems associated with the Brownlow stream.

- 'Business in the Community': Links with this organisation provided opportunities for community and statutory organisations to benefit directly from its expertise and contacts with the business sector.

- Community Business Programme: Negotiation led to this body, which offered a range of business services, extending into the Brownlow area.

- Social and Economic Development: The Worker developed a comprehensive economic strategy to direct the future of the project.

Women's projects consisted mainly of implementing measures to combat the social and economic isolation and exclusion of women in Brownlow, through supporting access to personal development opportunities, as well as training and employment. The work ensured that women's interests were promoted within statutory agencies and throughout the local community. Early in the programme the Project Worker established a Brownlow Women's Forum to help achieve its aims.   This was originally an information exchange and campaigning forum for local women, but a number of valuable projects emanated from this group, such as the Burnside Centre Planning Group, which led to the establishment of the Chrysalis Women's Centre – a focal point and catalyst for a wide range of activities and services – which was in turn supported and developed by the Project Worker. In recognition of the need for local women to gain qualifications and skills to increase their chance of obtaining secure and well-paid jobs, the project secured funding from the New Opportunities for Women initiative to provide a 36-week 'fast-track' course. This course showed that much could be achieved by women in a short space of time, given a suitable training environment. In order to promote this strategy for developing the issue of quality women's training, the Worker participated in a Northern Ireland-wide Women's Training Group, which had a planning and lobbying role. The project also established a young mothers' group for promoting personal development and improving service provision.

A Worker was employed by BCT to promote the take-up by young women of non-traditional areas of training and work – the first project of its kind in Northern Ireland, and it had considerable success in achieving this, particularly in relation to developments at the Government Training Centre and in schools.

The health project was involved in promoting participation by local people in health issues and in 'demystifying' the medical profession. While programmes of health awareness and promotion formed part of the output it attained two outstanding achievements. Firstly, it led to the establishment and development of a Health Centre Users' Group to enable the local population to maximise their participation in the planning and implementation of their health care. Secondly, was the establishment and development of a Lay Health Project. This project initially employed six local people to promote the key principles of partnership and participation in developing health and health-related programmes in the community. This involved working with the statutory agencies and community groups, as well as at an individual level in promoting and developing a holistic approach to health.

The health project also established a community health house which provided a number of resources for loan and consultation. This project became an important vehicle for the SHSSB to realise its programme of 'User Participation' at a local level. It attracted considerable interest from other projects, and was elected with five other areas in the UK to take part in a pilot study on the benefits of establishing a UK Child Health Network. It was also involved with the Northern Ireland Community Development and Health Network. The Health Project Worker also played a leading role in developing the Aldervale Project. This was an inter-agency community care initiative, managed by BCT, to develop a strategy for the inhabitants of a rehabilitated flats complex, ('many of whom are deemed to be at risk') with the support of a multi-agency and multidisciplinary committee.

Since its inception, the Trust was involved in providing valuable advice and support to a range of organisations providing playgroups and playschemes. The Borough Council agreed to assume responsibility for a BCT-funded pilot playscheme from 1993 onwards, and summer schemes flourished with the support of the Trust. Following the identification of particular needs through detailed research, a Play Policy Co-ordinator was appointed, who went on to establish a Working Party consisting of representatives of all the relevant agencies and organisations involved in play provision in the area. This Committee supported the Worker in producing a comprehensive 'mission statement' and a report containing specific recommendations on play, to be implemented by the relevant agencies. The Co-ordinator was also engaged in: a health and safety audit of play areas; assisting local play organisations with Trust funding applications; supporting the Summer Scheme Co-ordinator; assisting in the evaluation of the summer schemes; convening workshops on play; conducting a play survey and presenting the findings to a major play conference and the media; organising a 'play day' in which 1,500 people participated in a range of 'play' activities. The worker was also instrumental in forming a group for girls between the ages of eleven and fifteen and an After Schools Club for children aged between four and eleven. BCT supported the establishment and development of a local Play Association to ensure greater co-ordination and information exchange amongst different groups, and to attract more resources to the area.

The Information/Publicity Worker was responsible for producing twenty-three issues of 'Brownlow Matters' to highlight ongoing work, and provide information to a range of agencies/organisations and the local community. A number of basic information leaflets on aspects of its composition and role and a travelling exhibition were developed at an early stage to promote the work of the Project as well as a library of slides.

The community representatives also helped communicate the work of BCT to the wider community, and a series of seminars on the themes of 'partnership' and 'participation' were held to facilitate increased opportunities for local people and agency representatives to have a direct input to the Project's operations.

BCT caught the interest of senior policy-makers (including at Ministerial level) due mainly to its success at providing an integrated strategy of action through an established partnership. In this sense it also acted as a model of good practice for other community organisations. Its work was also publicised through the distribution of two Interim Reports to a range of government officials, politicians, academic bodies, community networks and the press. BCT staff also increased the lobbying voice of Brownlow by linking with others, and playing a leading role in a number of regional initiatives aimed at changing policy in order to benefit areas like Brownlow.

The final phase of the Project saw the employment of two additional Workers to launch new initiatives. One was concerned with developing a 'detached' youth project with young people deemed to be 'at risk' of offending. The other was a Community Education Project Worker whose aim was to provide training and skills to those involved in local community organisations.

The Key Issues

The achievements of the Project were considerable, although the functioning of the partnership did not always run smoothly. From the start there were suspicions and tensions between different community factions, between community partners and statutory agencies, between business and social interests, and between other professionals and BCT staff. In addition, despite their achievements there was at times, initially at least, some resentment towards staff from some of the local population and community organisations. The former, despite considerable community development credentials, would have been perceived as firmly in the statutory camp by the latter, and those staff who came from outside Brownlow (most of them) were widely regarded as interlopers. Some community representatives felt that the partnership was unequal, as resources were still largely in the hands of the statutory agencies. There was also the issue of community members feeling alienated from, or marginalised by, the dominant boardroom culture that included a form of discourse and procedure more familiar to professional agencies. Additionally, statutory agency workers were not sufficiently trained at the appropriate levels to embrace community development principles and practice. There were also profound ideological differences between those advocating a community enterprise strategy (such as the local economic development agency, Brownlow Limited) and the quasi-Marxist BCDA.

In relation to the development stage of Poverty Three, it was found that, despite the advances that had been made by BCT in developing a workable partnership and the activities emanating from that, there were still considerable problems with the Project. One factor that became apparent at this stage was that the obstacles to operating an innovatory practical partnership in a limited period (without a comprehensive lead-in stage, congruent with the demands of a programme like Poverty Three), while maintaining sensitivity to the particular circumstances of areas like Brownlow, could not be underestimated. In this sense, the dilemmas of the earlier US and British poverty programmes were being repeated. This underlined the need for the development of a 'total learning network' model of community education, with adult/community education providing the vehicle for improved communications and understanding between all those involved in addressing the problems of exclusion. In this sense, community development is itself essentially an educational process, and this, in turn, provides adult educators with new opportunities to play an important role in addressing the issues of social inequality and poverty, as well as contributing to the process of participatory democracy. The problems involved in developing the Brownlow partnership, in the developmental phase, illustrated the pitfalls of poverty programmes that do not include a substantial pre-development phase of community education. It also illustrated how this process needs to include all the actors involved, not just formal members of the partnership/board/committee, but all the significant members of staff from the project itself, the staff of community/voluntary organisations and, at the appropriate levels of responsibility, the staff of the statutory agencies involved.

Despite the examples of working partnership at this stage of the Project, it was still clearly flawed from the point of view of a significant section of the local representatives. If, as these representatives claimed, exclusion was not being reduced (or was being increased), then the principle of participation was not being adequately implemented, and partnership was little more than a form of tokenism. Yet the community development approach that the Project was adopting should have served to increase social inclusion and enable people to promote social change, rather than remain the recipients of a service provision approach (albeit dressed in a rhetoric of 'consumer' or 'community participation'). The underlying beliefs of community development indicate that there is a need for people to become the producers and agents of development in their communities, and that they can learn to be such. However, this requires a comprehensive programme of adult/community education specifically geared to the needs of the population in question, and one that challenges traditional assumptions about the nature of poverty and powerlessness.

In response to these issues, identified through the evaluation process, the Director of BCT produced the comprehensive paper on the implementation of partnership in Poverty Three (McDonough, 1992) which, in conjunction with the evaluation report, was to inform the work of the next phase of the Project. This was concerned with the actors reflecting on the experience to date, and using the experience in itself as a learning process for consolidating the partnership.

By the end of the fourth contractual period of the programme, BCT had consolidated its position in relation to meeting the requirements of Poverty Three. The range and output of the Trust itself, through the Project Workers' development of strategies with the target groups, and also through grant-aid to community organisations, was considerable. More importantly, in terms of the demands of the Programme and for the future of the organisation (and others for that matter), the novel approach to developing a workable partnership arrangement was operating much more smoothly. This was helped by the increased co-operation between agencies and the community, for which the Trust had acted as a major catalyst.

Maintaining a high profile, dissemination of information, encouraging and developing participation and constantly promoting the principles of Poverty Three, were together ensuring a much clearer understanding of the Project, and considerably smoothing what had, at times, been a precarious operation. By the summer of 1993, it had become clear that many of the initial objections to the Project had largely been resolved. Another important development was that community representatives on the Board had come to act in unison on almost all the important issues.

On the statutory side, the initial suspicion of the increased participation and empowerment that the Programme promoted had been largely eradicated, as professionals came to realise the potential in harnessing the skills of lay people, formulating agreed strategies with the community, and maximising synergy through inter-agency and statutory/community co-operation.

The need for a multidimensional analysis of, and approach to the problem of poverty came to be recognised by most of the major actors concerned. However, certain crucial issues still needed to be satisfactorily addressed. These included a number of the points made in the Project Director's earlier paper on partnership, and especially the power imbalance in the Trust, which was a barrier to empowerment. The continuing ideological divisions were also problematic. These illustrated some of the most fundamental differences between a community economic development or community enterprise strategy (such as Brownlow Limited, striving to promote a more positive image of the area), and a community action approach (the campaigning of the BCDA). Ironically, although the Trust was initially perceived by the BCDA to be closer to the ethos of Brownlow Limited (because of the statutory involvement), its approach (in highlighting the poor conditions of the area in order to campaign for more resources) was closer to that of the BCDA and a community development philosophy.

Throughout the final phase of the Programme in Brownlow, despite the successes of the Project, there remained serious difficulties in relation to the operation of the partnership. Not least of these was the continuing lack of involvement of the community partners in drawing up the criteria and conditions for individual projects, and the lack of training on the practicalities of partnership. These underlined again the necessity for a more elaborate role for a community education element in the development process, and a much closer cohesion between the two. There also continued to be misapprehensions around the control and/or flow of information, and this is always going to be a barrier to meaningful participation. Recurring themes, again echoing problems with previous anti-poverty initiatives, were the inhibitors to participation due to unequal access to resources, and questions concerning the 'representativeness' of community representatives. On top of all this, the staff found themselves in the unenviable position of trying to facilitate community proposals, at times quite radical, while having to work within the constraints of the Programme which were by no means totally flexible. Additionally, despite the efforts of the statutory representatives to facilitate practical partnership, they were still required to work within the restraints imposed by their respective agencies and increasing financial limitations.

In terms of generating enthusiasm and participation it was initiatives which appealed to the immediate perceived needs of the community that were the most successful. The work with women's' groups and children generated most immediate interest, and the most enthusiasm. In contrast to the attitudes to such initiatives, the requirements of the experimental nature of Poverty Three, and developing a 'strategic vision', were perceived to be remote; having formal access to participation and consultation was not enough to generate enthusiasm. The enhancement of community morale and esteem first needs to be achieved. This again underlines the lack of an adequate community education component in the process, and the need for this to be integrated with a comprehensive community development approach to promote empowerment. The community education initiative that was launched in the final phase of the Project came far too late, and should have been included at the start.

The lack of an effective economic strategy was another serious limitation after five years of the Programme. Undoubtedly a major limitation was the absence of key economic actors, which meant that the Project remained skewed to social and 'welfarist' interventions. Perhaps earlier development of the DOE's area plan (which came late in the Project) could have provided a focus and incentive for greater co-operation between the social and economic interests on the Board. An intensive Project like BCT could have provided an earlier opportunity for the DOE to pilot an approach that was participative, integrated and proactive, rather than focused primarily and almost exclusively on land use.

The Borough Council's economic strategy underlined the problem in effectively addressing poverty, given the level of joblessness and the need to create four times more jobs than the number envisaged by its somewhat optimistic proposals, in order to make any impression on the situation. It was also likely that Brownlow residents would be the last to get any jobs that were created in the council area, or at least they would only qualify for those of the most menial, low-paid, and short-term variety.

All of these issues raise the question of how to effectively address poverty without a comprehensive multidimensional approach. Yet this was one of the cornerstones of Poverty Three policy. The desire to get people back to work cannot be effectively tackled without recourse to the socio-cultural or familial environment. It is not just about individual training needs. The lack of an integrated socio-economic approach (including a total learning environment), in spite of the existence of a formal partnership, falls far short of attaining the goal of multidimensionality.

It became clear that, despite all the developments, the problems confronting the Brownlow community remained enormous, and only a long-term, sustained, integrated programme could create the conditions for a significant improvement in the quality of life of the community.

Conclusions

Due to the nature of Poverty Three, the form of the Brownlow Project, with its emphasis on evaluation and recording, allowed for the comprehensive analysis of its development. This was of vital importance, as it has been shown that while the systematic understanding of problems, and a strategic vision of aims and objectives, are preconditions for effective action, so too is the development of the knowledge and skills with which to act. The experience of Poverty Three in Brownlow illustrated that such knowledge and skills are frequently learned in the process of acting, hence the importance of the opportunity to reflect on action.

This allowed for an account of the development of a particular model of partnership and participation, and a discussion of how this particular model informs the contemporary debate on the nature and extent of these policy priorities and their practical implementation. Central to the discussion is the dual role of a specific form of community development/education in this process, and its implications for promoting empowerment, citizen participation and participatory democracy. In turn, these have a role in the development of a community policy designed to address such issues as social exclusion and fragmentation, poverty and inequality.

In order to realise this objective through the key vehicle of partnership, there is a need to include an explicit recognition of the need for an appropriate education and training programme for those working in agencies and organisations involved with the community. This needs to be implemented according to community development principles, and needs to precede attempts at creating formal partnership arrangements. This is best achieved within a 'total learning network' that ensures the co-ordination of all the relevant social, economic, educational and welfare services and agencies, and links them more effectively to local needs and interests. It also requires a form of educational provision that relates to the needs of the most disadvantaged sections of the population, and which pertains to the social action required in order to address such needs. Essentially, it should also be presented in an accessible manner, both structurally and in form and content, for those who are to benefit. This needs to adopt a model of community development/education that involves a synthesis of community work and community development, with an emphasis on creating new structures for community and social organisations. This not only involves using adult/community education to provide locally-based information, advice and resources on the one hand and facilitating learning relevant to social action on the other: it also involves addressing the issue of social exclusion, and facilitating active citizenship and effective participation.

This is why this Chapter was concerned with the relationship between community development and education and the role of both of these in the process of developing a practical partnership in order to optimise participation and multidimensionality. The role of community development and education needs to be considered in this process, because community development has guided previous anti-poverty initiatives, and its principles were widely adopted by Poverty Three. These principles were inextricably linked to community education in one form or another. Area-based programmes, harnessing the principles of community development and education, are essentially concerned with empowerment of the targeted people and facilitating their participation in addressing the issues of inequality, poverty and social exclusion. The relevance of this Chapter for contemporary policy is that in recent years it has been assumed that these issues can most effectively be addressed through the creation of area-based partnerships similar to the Poverty Three model. The lessons of the Brownlow experience should therefore have implications for other similar developments elsewhere, and the processes examined here should contribute to our understanding of the role of community development and education in programmes designed to address the issues of poverty and social exclusion.

References

Community Development Review Group (1991) Community Development in Northern Ireland: Perspectives for the Future, WEA, Belfast.

Gaffikin, F and Morrissey, M (1990) Northern Ireland: The Thatcher Years, Zed Books, London.

Gillespie, N (1994) Brownlow Community Trust: A Historical Account, BCT, Craigavon.

Lovett, T, Gillespie, N and Gunn, D (1995) Community Development, Education and Community Relations, University of Ulster, Jordanstown.

McDonough, R (1992) Working Paper for Discussion on Partnership as a Principle of the Third Poverty Programme, BCT, Craigavon.

McShane, L (1993) Community Support - A Pilot Programme, Northern Ireland Voluntary Trust, Belfast.

4

A Community Work Team in a Health & Social Services Trust

Martin O'Neill

The purpose of this Chapter is to encourage health and social services staff, social work educators, students, managers and practitioners to see that a community development perspective has an important role to play in the delivery of health and personal social services.

The reorganisation of health and personal social services in Northern Ireland in 1991 (DHSS, 1990) aimed to move services from a traditional, bureaucratically-dominated model, to one which embraced both the concepts of the marketplace, and policies which emphasised greater dialogue with local groups and communities. Craigavon and Banbridge Community Health & Social Services Trust (CBCHSST) was one of the newly-created entities of the government reforms. It was in the fortunate position, from a community development point of view, of having inherited the only team of community workers left in Northern Ireland statutory social services. This Team was the legacy of a strategy developed to meet the needs of the 'new' town of Craigavon in the 1970s, and the foresight of a management team which recognised the value of community development.

The Community Work Team as presently constituted, consists of a Senior Community Worker and two Community Workers. All three are professionally qualified Social Workers. The Team has administrative support and is situated within the Social Work Department based in a Health & Social Services Centre. The main aims of the Team are to promote a community development approach, and to strive to achieve and maintain positive working relationships between the Trust and the voluntary and community sectors, and to identify and help to meet health and social needs. These aims are consistent with the DHSS policy directives alluded to above. The Team works across all programmes of care and with all disciplines. Work is generated internally with Trust Staff, and externally through close links and co-operation with the voluntary and community sectors. The main thrust of the Team is to work with local people to identify health and social issues, needs, problems and potential solutions. Local people are assisted to develop the appropriate knowledge, skills and confidence to enable them to become more fully involved in the whole area of health and social wellbeing. In order to promote this work, the Team operates at strategic, operational and local levels. At the heart of its activity lies the keystone of empowerment.

The methods of working employed by the Team encompass the concept of 'community' defined by Barr et al (1996). Community work is seen as a generic term for a process of five interlinking elements (See Figure 1).

Figure 1

Community development emphasises the promotion of self-help, mutual support and empowerment.

Community action emphasises collective action by those adversely affected by policies. It entails challenging the status quo and developing alternative strategies.

Community services involves developing or changing services to make them more relevant or accessible to the community.

Community care involves the processes of assessing needs, profiling communities, identifying unmet need, establishing and enhancing support networks and contributing to planning, policy and practice within the fields of health and social care.

Community organisation involves improving communication, co-ordination and collaboration between agencies delivering services within a local community.

Empowerment

The existence of the Team makes a powerful contribution towards promoting interaction and a healthy working relationship between the Trust and the voluntary/community sectors. This work has demonstrated the potential to enable and empower communities to increase their self-confidence, awareness and self-reliance to start their own projects to meet identified needs, attract a range of funding, and manage projects with potentially sustainable futures.

According to the DHSS (1996) community empowerment has four core dimensions: personal empowerment; positive action; development of community organisations; and participation and involvement. These core dimensions serve as the 'acid test' for community work. In order to convert this rhetoric into action, the work of Couto (1997) on stages of empowerment is seen as helpful in providing tangible signs of local people becoming more confident, self-aware and powerful. These stages are: people discover they are not alone; supportive friendships develop; people start to define their situation in their own terms (stage of 'critical consciousness'); people start to represent themselves; they decide to oppose situations which are inappropriate; people think about independent solutions to problems and begin to take responsibility; people are faced with the limits of their empowerment and ability to achieve social change and possibly move in other directions.

The approach of the Community Work Team operates at a number of levels to help bring about the community empowerment as described above. These include direct community work assistance to grass roots community-based projects, and input and liaison with local and regional voluntary sector organisations. The Team also has a strong role within all statutory care programmes of Craigavon and Banbridge Community H&SS Trust: elderly and primary care, child and family care, mental health, and disability. In working directly with community organisations, Team Members work on a 'patch' basis, and have each developed a range of special interests and skills. The main focus of the Team is on community development approaches, and this work has been supported and defended at the highest level within the Trust (see DHSS, 1999).

The survival of the Community Work Team owes much to its ability to adapt to manage change and interpret policy in an imaginative way. The Team has made solid partnerships with a range of voluntary/community organisations. One of the results of this is that the

Trust has been able to use its limited financial resources to act as leverage for European Union Structural Funds and EU Special Support Programme for Peace and Reconciliation funding (for example: 25% Trust funding, bringing 75% EU funding to local voluntary/ community initiatives).

The Team has also taken a strong interest in identifying, complementing and working towards the achievement of the core business of the Trust. This has meant carefully balancing community work priorities and matching them with those of the Trust and the community/voluntary sector.

A number of examples taken from the recent work undertaken by the Team will illustrate both the range of activity and the enabling role which can be achieved by Community Workers working as part of a Health & Social Services agency.

Community Conference

One example of this work is the Community Work Team role in facilitating a conference on the Southern Health & Social Services Board (SHSSB) Draft Purchasing Prospectus 1997- 2000. This is an interesting example of how the Team has promoted a community development approach and principles up to Southern Health & Social Services Board level (SHSSB).

The Community Work Team were concerned that the SHSSB Draft Purchasing Prospectus contained little reference to the contribution of the voluntary/community sector towards health gain, or their importance in promoting health and social wellbeing in the community. There was also little mention of the value of community development in its own right. The Team were aware of the importance of the Final Purchasing Prospectus in setting priorities for the Health Social Services Trust, and that if community development received little attention, the role of the voluntary/community sector and the Team would be devalued and not supported. A Planning Group was set up with representatives of the major voluntary sector umbrella organisations in the area: Lurgan Council for Voluntary Action, Community Network Portadown, Moylinn House Community Development Support Services Agency, the Southern Health & Social Services Council and Craigavon Borough Council.

This Group planned the conference and prepared short briefing notes for the participants, which sought to inform them and stimulate ideas. This material included:- a short explanation of the activities and role of the Health & Social Services and its relationship with the voluntary/community sector; information on the World Health Organisation goals, Health for All 2000, and the World Health Organisation's support for a 'well informed, well motivated and actively participating community' as a key goal. Key information from Government policy included: The Strategy for the Support of the Voluntary Sector and for Community Development in Northern Ireland (1993) and DHSS (1996) Regional Strategy 1997-2002. This assisted in identifying issues, gaps, opportunities and questions to address community development during the conference.

The conference was a great success, more than seventy groups attended and the Southern Health & Social Services Board representative welcomed the opportunity to listen and discuss issues with those present. The Southern Health & Social Board responded positively by making community development a strategic objective in its final Purchasing Prospectus. This is now being operationalised by the Board, which is starting to develop its Community Development Strategy together with Health & Social Services Trusts.

A number of key issues contributing to the effectiveness of this consultation process were: the role of the Community Work Team and the proactive way in which it drew attention to the importance of the purchasing document; the role of the voluntary umbrella organisations in cascading down information to smaller community groups; the involvement of the Health & Social Services Council in assisting this process; support from the Trust Chief Executive; the inclusion of the main recommendations from the conference to the Southern Health & Social Services Board to prioritise community development and further recognise the work of the voluntary/community sector. It was also important to acknowledge the value of groups and agencies working together to tackle issues and problems (see DHSS, 1999).

The SHSSB has also stated that it will seek to work with the H&SS Trusts to address the following key areas. It wishes to embrace the community development principles of participation, empowerment, equity, partnership and collective action. The promotion of supporting community infrastructure to enable better individual and community participation will be addressed. The SHSSB have given a commitment of extra funding and resources to achieve these aims (SHSSB Purchasing Prospectus 1997-2000).

The impact of the conference on the community and voluntary sector has also been to heighten awareness and transfer knowledge and information on Health & Social Services responsibilities between Boards and Trusts. These outcomes demonstrate the effectiveness in having a community development presence within Health & Social Services who can look beyond the sometimes narrow 'health agenda' or 'programme of care agenda', and act as a facilitator/broker/advocate.

The above example demonstrates the ability of the Community Work team to work in partnership, and promote participation at a range of levels. This approach is taken by the Team with a wide range of community/voluntary sector projects and initiatives which have a direct and indirect relationship with Health & Social Services. Examples include: developing carers' groups and initiatives; initiating needs analysis and research into health and social need; work within all care programmes: elderly and primary care, child and family care, mental health and disability. The role of the Team often starts as a highly active catalyst with a new project, and gradually moves through a process of enabling, to that of a liaison and maintenance role with a group or organisation.

The following examples demonstrate how a community development approach can assist in identifying and meeting health and social needs. These case examples are illustrative of the model developed by Popple (1995).

CASE EXAMPLE: Child and Family Care

The Community Work Team's work with the Southern Travellers' Early Years Partnership (STEP) involves community development, community organisation and anti-oppressive work with an ethnic minority group on early years issues. Travellers are a recognised ethnic minority group in Ireland with a shared history, customs and values. STEP was established in mid-1995 to bring together four local support groups to build a partnership for community development support for Travellers in the Southern Health & Social Services Board. Research has identified that Traveller children face considerable disadvantage from their early years onward. The lack of access to educational and other support places barriers in the way of Traveller children and their parents, and compounds problems in primary and secondary school and later life.

STEP works in a context of multiple disadvantage faced by Travellers, and aims to overcome the previous lack of co-ordination between the four Traveller organisations and statutory bodies in the Southern Health & Social Services Board's area, in order to benefit Traveller children. The role of the Senior Community Worker is to act as a Health & Social Services representative and partner in STEP, and to provide line management support to the Co-ordinator. Chapters 7 and 8 describe work with Travellers in the area.

CASE EXAMPLE: Mental Health

The Community Work Team work with Friends and Carers Engaged (FACE) in the areas of community care, community development and community organisation. FACE is a mental health support group for carers of people with schizophrenia and manic depression. This self-help carers' support network was created on the initiative of the carers themselves, together with Health & Social Services Staff.

The community work role consisted of facilitating an initial informal meeting with the group to get to know them, listen and clarify with them what they identified as their main issues and problems. Some of these were the need to build mutual support and information sharing, developing understanding, sharing experiences, stress relief, financial hardship and stigma.

Several natural leaders were recognised, and it was decided to form a small Working Group to take forward some of these issues. A number of meetings were held and the Community Worker facilitated the discussion which began as a first ideas exercise, and worked towards an action plan which the group wanted to be practical and achievable. It emerged that the group wanted to offer a wide range of support and services, and to achieve this a Co-ordinator would be required.

The community work role was to assist in formalising the group and facilitating the writing of a Constitution for charitable status. This would enable the group to apply to charitable Trust Funds. A potential funder, The Northern Ireland Voluntary Trust, EU Special Support Programme for Peace and Reconciliation, was identified, and the group met with their Assessment Officer and presented their case (without the Community Worker being present). Further encouragement and guidance was given at that meeting, and other tasks and issues to be undertaken included: thinking about what the group wanted the worker to do, writing down issues and re-setting priorities; and training on, and discussion around a range of issues of group development and organisation. The group also engaged with people with mental health problems to obtain their views and ideas about the new project, and maximise their participation

This work involved a tremendous amount of voluntary activity in the space of a year, and illustrates the potential of community development to engage and support local people facing challenges, difficulties and maximising opportunities in the mental health field. Chapter 11 describes the mental health partnership, including FACE.

CASE EXAMPLE: Building Community Infrastructure

Work with Community Network Portadown involved community organisation, community development and community relations. Portadown is a town which has a strong tradition of voluntary and community activity. However, it has also been racked by civil strife and sectarianism. The Community Work Team helped to identify the need for a network organisation in Portadown to assist and support the wide variety of community and voluntary sector projects in the area.

Many groups in the area tended to work without a great deal of co-operation or co-ordination between them. Following consultation between community leaders, Craigavon Borough Council and Community Work Team, it was decided to work towards the building of a new cross-community alliance for the voluntary and community sectors in the town, and its rural hinterland. The reasons identified for such an organisation were: the need for greater networking; sharing resources and expertise; promotion of community relations; fund-raising; lobbying statutory agencies and ensuring a collective voice for the community/ voluntary sector.

The Working Group convened a public meeting to consult widely on the proposal. At the meeting more than sixty groups were represented, and the existing Working Group were given a mandate to move forward with the idea and act as a Steering Group. The Community Work Team supported the Group to draw up a draft Constitution, elect officers at the inaugural Annual General Meeting, and enable local groups to join the new network.

Funding was obtained through Craigavon and Banbridge Community H&SS Trust, Craigavon Borough Council and Northern Ireland Voluntary Trust, for a Worker and an Administrator. A shop front base is now operating in the town centre, which provides advice and support, administrative assistance and desk top publishing for members. Community Network Portadown publishes regular newsletters to all its constituent groups. Its long term aim is to develop a new community resource centre and promote community development and community relations in the town. Chapter 2 has further details on the work of the Network.

Targeting Resources

The Community Work Team has responded to the requirement on the Health & Social Services Trust to target resources to those most in need. The above example is a good illustration of its role in intervention in an area requiring improved community infrastructure.

Meeting Local Need

The Team has a strong track record in working with communities to facilitate them to identify and articulate their own needs. Identifying specific local needs is a key part of this work, and methods include the following: identifying localities or groups that have clearly unmet needs or a weak community infrastructure. This has led some areas to be bypassed by major funding initiatives, as they have not had the capacity to make their case to the relevant funders. The Team also respond to requests and engage with Trust Directors, Managers and Staff for assistance with particular developmental issues or problems.

Partnerships

The Team has had a proactive role over the years in initiating and facilitating community networks and umbrella organisations in the area. Examples include: Community Network Portadown (CNP), Lurgan Council for Voluntary Action (LCVA) and Banbridge & District Community Network (BDCN).

Community Development Outcomes

Major community development outcomes of the work of the Community Work Team are evidenced in the 'Mainstreaming Community Development' document (DHSS, 1999).

Some of these are:

- The commitment of the Southern Health & Social Services Board to a strategic community development approach.

- The commitment by Craigavon and Banbridge Community H&SS Trust to community development principles and practice.

- The Senior Community Worker's role on the DHSS Community Development Working Group (Northern Ireland), which has recently produced its Final Report on Mainstreaming Community Development in Health and Social Services (1999).

- The establishment of a variety of community development networks and partnerships in the Craigavon and Banbridge areas, and their potential to engage with the Trust and other agencies on priorities.

- The work of the Team in raising awareness of Health & Social Services agendas with the voluntary/community sector, and facilitating higher levels of inputs to the Southern Health & Social Services Board and Trust.

The impact of the Community Work Team was noted by external consultants conducting a baseline study of community development in Northern Ireland (DHSS, 1999):

> *"Of all the areas of Northern Ireland Health & Social Services Boards, the Southern Health & Social Services Board, and in particular the Craigavon and Banbridge Community H&SS Trust, have demonstrated a consistent commitment to the principles of community development...now espoused by Well Into 2000"*

> *"These all reflect a net increase in the outputs of community development activity that would be unlikely to have happened, at least at the same pace, in the absence of the team."*

This achievement occurred at a time when community development was not considered as part of 'core business' of health and social services, and during a climate of cutbacks and pressure on resources in such services in Northern Ireland. The members of the Team themselves, and the Chief Executive, attribute the strong community development focus and the survival and consolidation of the work of the Team to the following factors: a commitment to the values of community development and belief in its effectiveness; adaptability, or 'an ability of the team to constantly reinvent itself'; capacity to leverage resources, evidenced by their 'quantified' success in drawing in real additional resources to the area; and relevance, or the ability to identify specific aspects of work programmes and project activities that directly address the Trust's priorities, as well as those of the target groups which it intends to serve; innovation - staff have worked hard to identify new opportunities for activity, staying constantly aware of new ideas and approaches, and researching funding opportunities and alternative methodologies for achieving the Team's and the Trust's desired outcomes.

An example of this is the Team's support for an initiative on 'social firms', described in Chapter 12. This has involved substantial amounts of research, including investigating examples of how such approaches have been used elsewhere in the UK and beyond. The Team has also carried out active networking with relevant statutory, voluntary and community agencies. Presentation - the Team has managed to present itself through the mechanism of its annual business plan as 'an asset rather than a liability'. Team Members see themselves as having to 'sell' the value of their service, and the community development approach that is integral to their way of working, to other colleagues within hard-pressed programme of care areas on an ongoing basis. This pressure has in itself contributed to their will and ability to survive.

> *"The Team has proved durable and creative, stable and innovative. It has demonstrated its effectiveness not just by citing its involvement in various community development projects, and through its adoption and promotion of community development approaches and good practice, but also by producing a business plan mapping out its contribution to the work of the Trust in terms which non-community development practitioners, and those interested in 'value for money' issues, can relate to."*

(DHSS, 1999)

Conclusion

Community development has an increasingly important role to play within health and social services. The author would contend that the value bases of community development and health care, social care and social work have broad similarities, and that the principles of partnership, engagement and empowerment with people can happen by using community development approaches.

We would therefore encourage H&SS Managers and Health and Social Workers to revisit community development and use its varied approaches in their attempts to engage more meaningfully with local people and communities. In this way health and personal social services can become less stigmatising, build more positive relationships with those marginalised from society, promote social inclusion and continue to move from a service-led to a needs-led perspective. As the Government itself states:

> *"Community development involves supporting local communities to identify the health and social concerns of greatest importance to them and helping them devise and implement solutions. The Government wishes to see community development further extended, strengthened and provided throughout Northern Ireland and mainstreamed in all health and social services agencies"*

> (DHSS, 1996)

Implementing this community development strategy will lead to the achievement of improved health and social wellbeing in Northern Ireland.

It is therefore crucial to the development of community work as a vibrant, constructive method of engaging with local people and communities that experiences are shared, and opportunities are made available to learn from others. Only then will we be able to develop our own practice.

Please note:

While Craigavon/Banbridge is used to illustrate contemporary examples of community work/community development it is important to acknowledge that: good practice exists in other geographical areas; there are many examples of good practice in other Trusts and Boards and in the voluntary/community sector; and each locality is different and has its own needs, characteristics, strengths and circumstances.

References

Couto R A (1997) cited in 'Process-focused, Product-focused Community Planning...' by E Sadan and A Churchman in <u>Community Development Journal</u>, Volume 32, No 1 January.

Department of Health & Social Services (1990) <u>People First</u>, HMSO, Belfast.

Department of Health & Social Services (1993) <u>Government Strategy for the Support of the Voluntary Sector and for Community Development in Northern Ireland</u>, DHSS, Northern Ireland.

Department of Health & Social Services (1996) <u>Monitoring and Evaluation of Community Development in Northern Ireland</u>, Voluntary Activity Unit, DHSS, Northern Ireland.

Department of Health & Social Services (1996) <u>Regional Strategy 1997-2002</u>, DHSS, Belfast.

Department of Health & Social Services (1999) <u>Mainstreaming Community Development in Northern Ireland</u>, DHSS, Belfast.

Popple, K (1995) <u>Analysing Community Work: Its Theory and Practice</u>, Open University Press, Buckingham.

Southern Health & Social Services Board (1995) <u>Director of Social Services: Sixth Assessment of Need - 1995</u>, Armagh, SHSSB.

Southern Health & Social Services Board (1997) <u>Purchasing Prospectus 1997-2000</u>, SHSSB, Armagh.

World Health Organisation (1986) Ottawa Charter for Health Promotion - <u>Health for All 2000</u>, WHO.

5   Community Development Facilitated by a Rural General Practice: The Ballyward Experience

Fergal O'Brien, Nicola Hodge, Alan Deane, Dr Alastair Chestnutt, Janet Davidson, Liam O'Flaherty, Yvonne Spiers, Eamonn Keenan, Dr Brid Farrell, Liz Hanna

Introduction

The Chapter charts the course of the development of the Garran and Croob Cross Community Association from its origin in a primary care needs assessment of the area in June 1996, through to the appointment of a Development Worker in November 1997.

The aims of the Chapter are to explore the meaning of community development across a range of primary care disciplines; to examine the contribution of a rural general practice in facilitating community development; to critically examine Rapid Participatory Appraisal (RPA) as a method of needs assessment; to locate the Garran and Croob experience within Health & Social Services policies; and to explore ideas around the future of community development within primary care.

Background to Ballyward

Of the seventeen wards in Banbridge District Council, Ballyward is the only one registered as 'disadvantaged' under the Robson Indices (Robson et al,1994). In Northern Ireland its ranking on the Robson indices of deprivation would place it within the top 37.9%. The Ballyward ward has incorporated the former Garran and Croob wards since 1992, when the Boundaries Commission last reviewed local government ward boundaries (see Figure 1). It is a dispersed rural area encompassing many small townlands and villages across a mountainous area in the Dromara Hills.

In the 1991 Census, the population of the Garran area was 3,924, comprising 1,131 households. Of the 2,925 people who responded to the question on 'religion' in the census, 33.3% said they were Catholic and 57.6% Protestant. Of the population 86% were employed in one of five industry types as follows:

Other Services	26%
Agriculture, Fishing, Forestry	18%
Construction	17%
Catering/Distribution	13%
Other manufacturing	13%

Approximately 35.7% travelled to work outside of their District Council area, compared to the Northern Ireland average of 28%.

During the Southern Health & Social Services Board needs assessment it was found that the area had no broad-based community groups, no playgroup and only three registered childminders. There was one mother and toddler group in Ballyward Parish Church Hall and a carers group in the local GP surgery. Other facilities include a GAA Hall, Catholic Church Hall and Church of Ireland Hall.

In summary, the area had poor community infrastructure, and opportunities for cross-community contact were limited. One notable exception in the area was the local GP surgery used by all sections of the community.

Policy and Funding Context

The Ballyward needs assessment was conducted in the context of the Regional Strategy for Health and Social Wellbeing 1997-2002 (DHSS, 1996), and the community association formed during the period when the then new Labour Administration in Northern Ireland published Well into 2000 (DHSS, 1997), a companion document to the Regional Strategy. Both documents include considerable references to community development. The Regional Strategy charges Trusts not only to develop ways of monitoring the provision of community care, but also to audit and assess the effectiveness of health and social care interventions.

In Northern Ireland many new opportunities existed for cross-community and community development work as a result of Peace and Reconciliation monies from Europe following the 1994 ceasefires. In public sector spending all departments were concerned with the concept of 'targeting health and social need', ie ensuring that limited resources reached those communities most in need. The needs assessment methodology employed is addressed in the following section.

Ballyward Primary Care-Based Needs Strategy

A locally-based Rapid Participatory Appraisal of health and social needs was carried out by a Community Worker, District Nurse Team Leader and two local residents in Ballyward. This resulted from a joint initiative between the Department of Health Strategy and Primary Care in the Southern Health & Social Services Board and the Craigavon and Banbridge Community H&SS Trust Community Work Team. A key factor which influenced the agenda of both agencies was the Robson Report (Robson et al,1994) which highlighted Ballyward as the only designated 'disadvantaged' ward out of seventeen within Banbridge District Council.

The needs survey used qualitative and quantitative approaches. Participants were drawn from a range of geographical locations within the area. The questionnaire comprised of sixty-one questions covering the following topics: community composition, community infrastructure, physical environment, socio-economic factors, disease and disability, health and social services, health-policy and open-ended questions which allowed people to say what changes they would like to make in the area.

Twenty-six people were interviewed. Issues of concern which emerged from the survey included lack of transport, social isolation, the need for facilities for older people, improved access to health and social services, and the desire for adult education classes. From responses, 42% identified the need for a cross-community venue, 19% pre-school facilities, 15% an elderly day centre and 8% adult education classes. A summary of this research is contained in the Annual Report of the Director of Public Health (SHSSB, 1996).

When the results of the survey were fed back to participants by the SHSSB, the Community Worker then posed the question whether people would be interested in forming a local group to take action on the results. As a result of the willingness shown from the survey participants a Steering Group was formed in order to create the new Community Association and seek funding for a Development Worker to take forward the Committee's concerns. The name chosen by the local people changed initially from the 'Ballyward and District Community Association' to the 'Garran and Croob Cross Community Association' to reflect the cross-community ethos.

Table 1 summarises what happened from the point of feedback of the survey results, to the establishment of the Garran and Croob Cross Community Association.

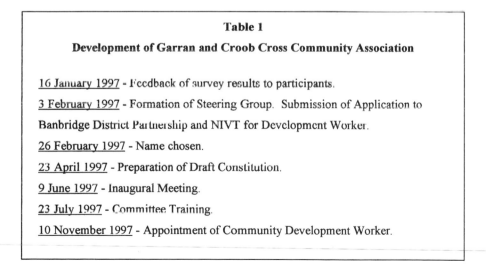

Table 1

Development of Garran and Croob Cross Community Association

16 January 1997 - Feedback of survey results to participants.

3 February 1997 - Formation of Steering Group. Submission of Application to Banbridge District Partnership and NIVT for Development Worker.

26 February 1997 - Name chosen.

23 April 1997 - Preparation of Draft Constitution.

9 June 1997 - Inaugural Meeting.

23 July 1997 - Committee Training.

10 November 1997 - Appointment of Community Development Worker.

The process and outcomes of the community needs assessment will now be examined from a range of perspectives including: Craigavon and Banbridge Community H&SS Trust Community Worker, District Nursing Team Leader, Social Work Team Leader Older Persons', Health Visitor; Garran and Croob Cross Community Association Development Worker, Ballyward General Practitioner and Business Manager and the Public Health Perspective at the Southern Health & Social Services Board.

Multidisciplinary Perspectives on the Ballyward Experience

The Perspective of Craigavon and Banbridge Community Health & Social Services Trust Community Work Team

Community development interest in the Ballyward area from the Craigavon and Banbridge Community H&SS Trust Community Work Team originated in 1994, when day care and fieldwork Social Work Staff from the elderly programme of care approached the team in order to develop a social centre for older people in the area. However, it became apparent that there was neither a suitable neutral venue, nor a local group to take forward this idea.

The Community Work Team were on the point of undertaking a community profile in the area when they learned about the SHSSB's plans to do a needs assessment using the Rapid Participatory appraisal method (Scott Murray, 1995). From the community work perspective the Team were keen to avoid duplication, and readily agreed to work with the Southern Health & Social Services Board on its needs assessment. The Rapid Participatory Appraisal method incorporated three core elements of community development: inter-agency work between the Board and Trust, multidisciplinary work (between nursing, community work and social work), and local participation through the engagement of two local people by the Community Worker who was involved in the research process from its inception.

Meetings were held with Banbridge District Council Officers in the Economic Development Department with a full acknowledgement that the Ballyward area had been earmarked in the Council's Local Economic Development Strategy (Banbridge District Council, 1994) as an area of disadvantage which the Council would be interested in regenerating.

As the research neared completion, contact with Banbridge District Council intensified and its Economic Development Workers began to take an increasingly significant role in partnership with the Community Worker in developing the new Community Association.

The role of statutory community workers encompasses supporting diverse voluntary and community groups within Trust boundaries. It was important to assist the Garran and Croob Cross Community Association in obtaining the services of their own Development Worker, who would provide a commitment to local people's concerns. A key role played by the Craigavon and Banbridge Community H&SS Trust Community Worker was to act as intermediary between local people, Trust professionals and representatives from other agencies.

Perspective of Economic Development Worker, Banbridge District Council
The Banbridge Local Economic Development Strategy was developed in 1995 for the period 1995-1999. The Strategy is the result of intensive consultation by a team appointed by Banbridge District Council, with a wide range of interested parties taking into consideration the statistical background, together with the opinions of those who live and work in the area. The Local Economic Development Strategy underpins all the Economic Development activity in the Banbridge District, and embedded within the Strategy is the theme of 'community economic development'.

The socio-economic conditions show that Banbridge overall is relatively well off in terms of a number of key indicators, compared with the regional average. However, these averages conceal potential pockets of greater deprivation within the Council area. Garran is one of the wards where deprivation exists, but until 1994, little work had been done because of the lack of community infrastructure.

In 1994, a public meeting was held in the surgery at Ballyward. The community was keen to create local animation and to do 'something' in their district. Out of initial meetings the Garran and Croob Cross Community Development Association was formed, with a remit for regenerating the area. One of the key tasks was identifying funding, and securing the services of a Development Worker. From this point onwards, Banbridge District Council Staff along with the Health & Social Services staff, played a facilitating role in this rapid development.

From a District Council perspective, working alongside the statutory agencies and the community allowed Banbridge District Council to work with the Garran and Croob district, the only officially deprived area in the district.

The Economic Development Manager, Community Economic Development Officer and Community Relations Officer were key players in assisting the community to come together to make an application to the Banbridge District Partnership for the employment of a Development Worker.

District Nursing Team Leader Perspective

The Primary Care Health Care Team has been involved in various initiatives in the Ballyward area prior to the present survey. The King's Fund Organisational Audit took place between June 1994 and March 1995 in the local GP practice. In May 1995, the District Nursing Team Leader completed research on the needs of carers.

As a result of two previous initiatives, carers in Ballyward were offered the Training for Carer's course, which occurs twice-yearly in the Banbridge locality. The course continues to be organised by the Development Officer of the Banbridge Carers' Support, the Social Work Team, District Nurse Team Leaders and the Banbridge Occupational Therapy Department. The course in Ballyward commenced in September 1995, and was held in the local GP surgery as it was the only neutral venue in the area. It was arranged over a twelve-week period and involved professionals who worked in the area. This led to Banbridge Area Carers Support Group forming a Support Group for carers in the Ballyward area. The services provided include a monthly Support Group meeting, social events and other courses.

The needs assessment gave the District Nurse an opportunity to view a cross section of the area, and the people who lived and worked there. From a district nursing point of view there were certain areas of particular interest within the different sections.

The section on physical environment was important for a number of reasons, as the condition and type of housing can affect how we are able to practise within patients' homes. It can limit a patient's rehabilitation if the home environment is very small or on a number of levels.

If sanitary conditions are poor, it can result in extra equipment being needed. Furthermore, if manual handling is necessary and extra equipment is needed, the environment is very important.

Transport is important both from patient and district nurse perspectives. A patient may be unable to get to the surgery because of lack of transport, and this can increase the workload of the district nurse. The lack of sufficient public transport can obviously increase social isolation, and can also restrict the population's ability to attend organised meetings, therefore restricting full participation within the community.

The section from the survey on disease and disability can form part of the health profile for the area. It can also be used as part of a health promotion strategy through such channels as the Carers' Support Group.

The consumer's view of health and social services is very important, as it allows a more balanced view between patient and professional regarding what services are available and how these are accessed. The whole emphasis in the White Paper 'People First' (DHSS, 1990) is on 'needs-led' as opposed to 'service-led' assessment and patient participation. Therefore, the evidence from the research is a very valuable tool in allowing debate between professionals on whether or not they are responding in this way, and also meeting the requirements in the Patients' Charter (DHSS, 1991).

As the District Nursing Team Leader had been involved in the implementation of the research, she was aware of the most common problems that the people of the area had. The fact that 50% of the responses felt social isolation was a problem both for the elderly and mothers with young children, could be related to two different areas. Firstly, 81% of those questioned had difficulty with transport due to lack of public transport, needing two cars and perhaps not owning a car. In addition, the condition of some of these rural roads was not considered to be very good.

This type of user participatory research has proved to be very successful because the users in partnership with the professionals working in the area, have taken it forward. District nurses, due to the demands of the job can become very focused on their own caseloads and fail to see the bigger picture. This, in turn, prevents further caseload planning and restricts them in being proactive, and therefore they remain reactive. Research such as this will enable this to change.

This research, together with the routine data collection, forms part of the health needs assessment for the area. This ensures health is a live issue and enables community nurses to take on new challenges and skills in response to changing health care needs.

Social Work Perspective

As members of the Primary Care Team, the Social Work Team for Older Persons are also involved in the provision of services within the Ballyward area. Traditionally, from the social work perspective, services have been provided from an individual/family casework orientation. Since 1994, attempts were made unsuccessfully to combat social isolation amongst the elderly by establishing a locally-accessible social centre. However, there were two main obstacles to the development of such a facility: the lack of a readily identifiable community group, and the lack of premises that were seen to be cross-community.

Our team was involved, on a multidisciplinary basis, in successful work within this area; such as a King's Fund audit of the local GP practice, and the establishment of a local Carers' Group. With the inception of the community development approach, we have acquired a broader view of the needs of the area through the involvement of the local community.

The benefits that accrue from this broader perspective include user participation in an organised way, and the added value that such partnerships bring in terms of shared resources. The effects of working in partnership with the local community are enhanced public relations and understanding between the community and the whole Primary Care Team. This, in turn leads to a better exchange of information, both in terms of the identification of assessed needs and the locally-targeted provision of services to meet those needs in partnership with the community.

From a broader perspective of needs assessment involving the local community, the focus must now move to looking at a needs assessment involving older people. This will look at areas like social isolation and the provision of a locally-based centre - but this time having started from the broader remit which community development brings.

Health Visiting Perspective

From a health visitor perspective, health visitors have a role to identify health needs of individuals and whole populations, while maintaining a client caseload. This means having a local knowledge base. The appraisal of health needs identified in the Garran and Croob area reflected the views of local people and has subsequently given them a sense of ownership, empowerment and control over health and social issues which affect their lives. This is an opportunity to see the underlying pattern of health need that can influence health strategies and long-term strategic planning for this area. For example, the local Association, through its action plan, has already identified needs relating to the elderly, pre-school provision, women's health, the environment, youth and economic development.

Although many of these issues would reflect the existing agenda of local statutory agencies, the most significant aspect of the Garran and Croob experience is the fact that local people now have ownership of these concerns.

The GP Perspective

The GP Practice covers much of the population in the area and has always looked after all sections of the community.

The area of Garran and Croob had been identified by the Robson report as being a disadvantaged area. The Council (Banbridge) and Health Board (Southern Health & Social Services Board) of this area began looking for ways to counter this. There was not a community group which covered the area both geographically and socially to which they could address themselves. The 'disadvantaged' status would give such a group enhanced prospects of funding for projects to help the population.

Previously there have been examples of the community as a whole working together in shared areas of common need. Examples are: a Fundraising Committee for medical equipment for the Ballyward Practice had been very effective for many years; and there was a rapid and effective cross-community mobilisation to oppose the development of a 'burn house' in the area.

The GP was consulted on the needs assessment survey and subsequent developments by Banbridge District Council and the Southern Health & Social Services Board, which helped to raise funds for a Development Worker. The Worker's role was: helping to facilitate interested persons in the area in forming a Cross Community Association by offering a 'neutral venue' for the initial meetings; offering clerical and administrative support and a personal commitment to meetings.

The GP hopes that problems identified via the Rapid Participatory Appraisal carried out in the embryonic stages of the Association (social isolation, transport problems and problems of care of the elderly in the community) which impinge on his work, will be addressed by the Association in co-operation with statutory and voluntary bodies.

Practice Business Manager Perspective

Before setting off on the Ballyward Surgery's Management perspective of this development journey, it is important to be clear about the Practice's underlying philosophy and rationale, the direction set by a Total Quality Management (TQM) strategy, and also what preparations have been made to ensure its success.

A common definition of total quality is: *"Everyone is involved, at all levels and across all functions, in ensuring quality in everything they do."* This total quality approach is consistent with the community development approach which the Practice has facilitated.

Putting the Foundations and Goals in Place

Ballyward Surgery embarked upon this journey early in 1994 by developing for itself a quality management system and an agreed 'mission statement', 'vision' and set of 'values'. These then gave focus and influence to subsequent decision-making and action plans for the surgery-based team. We were, however, aware that the provision of primary health care is, necessarily, the business of multidisciplinary teamworking, and recognised the need to integrate more with both patient/client groups and other health service providers.

The Ballyward Practice participated in the King's Fund Organisation Audit (KFOA) between the summer of 1994 and the spring of 1995. This process required close inspection of current practice and how we related and communicated with our patients and other health care professionals. Essentially, it became a fast track vehicle for Ballyward Surgery and

Community Staff to provide clear direction and goals, establish objectives, priorities, standards and values, lead by example and live our 'values'.

The phase that followed resulted from the combined direct input of Craigavon and Banbridge Community H&SS Trust (CBCHSST) and the Public Health consultants from the SHSSB. They approached us with the exciting prospect of carrying out a qualitative Community Needs Assessment within a geographical area that represented a high percentage of our patient population. 'Rapid Participatory Appraisal' (RPA) was the chosen method. Given our 'mission, vision and values' statements, and our determination to focus in upon meeting patient's *actual* rather than *perceived* needs, the Practice was extremely keen to support and facilitate in any way possible. The idea of facilitating processes that supported and reached out to the wider Ballyward community sat very comfortably with our Surgery's vision and philosophy.

Naturally, to be fully representative, the RPA method required cross-community involvement and key informers from diverse groups. These diverse groups required to meet, and as a minimum start to the process, required a 'neutral venue' meeting place. I believe the availability, or not, of a neutral venue is the rock upon which cross-community activity can either be established or perish!

Some practical considerations for the local Practice Team were: How many people could be safely accommodated in the Surgery building? - advice was sought and obtained from the local Fire Authority; Was there a keyholder available to open and close the building - usually after normal opening hours?; If no keyholder was presently available, was anyone flexible enough and responsive to change; Were there budget or financial considerations for the practice?; How long could the Practice facilitation be sustained?; Were there additional security considerations during or as a result of the Practice facilitation.

In Ballyward's case, the energy and enthusiasm brought by the Community Worker representing C&BCHSST ensured successful outcome of the launch and implementation of the RPA! His energy and enthusiasm was such as to be infectious, resulting in everyone involved operating, almost from the off, as an effective Team Member sharing a common vision and a common goal. We have been privileged, and the local community benefited, by having such a gifted individual lead and guide through previously 'uncharted waters'.

On completion of the RPA some big decisions had to be made. We had gathered the qualitative data of the RPA, attached to it quantitative data from the Doctor's clinical database, and essentially presented ourselves with a choice - to act upon the data and prepare a consequential action plan, or, ignore it and walk away, albeit with the positive experience of having succeeded in bringing the community together in a common cause. Perhaps in some instances, implementing a first time cross-community common cause can be deemed in itself a success.

Again, under the guidance of the same C&BCHSST Community Worker, the required agencies and individuals were brought together at Ballyward Surgery, resulting in the establishment of the present Garran and Croob Cross Community Association. Efforts continued, and the new Association appointed a part-time Community Development Worker, primarily to champion our identified action plan, but also to innovate, network and liaise with national, regional and local common agendas. The resultant action plans of both Garran and Croob Cross Community Association and Ballyward Surgery remain under continuous review.

My involvement as a self-employed Business Manager within a primary care setting, and my experience as an individual living within an isolated rural community, reinforce my beliefs around collective team workings, the sharing of common visions and goals, and the importance of measurement within management. *"If you cannot measure, you cannot manage."* Anon.

Public Health Perspective

Primary care is a natural starting point for identifying local needs. General practitioners have frequent contact with patients and control access to secondary care services. As providers of services, they are ideally placed to respond to local needs through practice-based initiatives. Primary care can provide local information about the health of the practice population.

Community assessment using a Rapid Participatory Appraisal approach facilitates obtaining the views of local people on their health needs, existing services and the resources available in a community, eg playgroups. Health services play a minor role in improving the health of populations through the empowerment of local communities, taking account of the important influences of other factors such as lifestyle, education and employment on the health of the population.

This approach should ensure better delivery of health services, facilitate the development of local strategies to address local health problems, and develop community participation.

Perspective of Garran and Croob Cross Community Association's Development Worker

The support of the Primary Care Team to the development of the Garran and Croob Cross Community Association in Ballyward was essential and crucial in a number of areas. The support of the GP and Practice Staff provided resources at a practical level, in that the group lacked a room for meetings and access to photocopying facilities. The Staff Team at the Surgery was also a resource to the group, with particular respect to skills of planning, prioritising and management. These resources were essential, especially in the early stages of the group's development. However, this support has continued after the group acquired its own premises and accessed funding for equipment.

Following the initial research, it was identified that the Surgery was the one neutral building located in the area. Therefore, the use of Surgery premises also provided legitimacy and a mandate to the group in different, but important ways. As a group wishing to establish its credibility as a genuinely cross-community-based organisation, the Surgery's neutrality was of particular importance. A primary care focus provided an opportunity to develop cross-community work based on an issue that is potentially neutral. Health is a less contested issue for local populations from different traditions and has the potential for co-operation. For example, local campaigns against the closure of hospitals have attracted support from all sections of the community.

Secondly, it was also recognised that support to the group by Surgery Doctors and other staff provided legitimacy of status to the group's establishment and purpose. This support also contributed to and supported the community group to establish health issues as a core part of their agenda.

Indications from the experience of the group would strongly suggest that inter-professional approaches to primary health care within a community development perspective can have positive outcomes. Community development has implications about the role of the professional in supporting an integrated and responsive approach to the needs of the community.

At a broader policy level suggested by 'Fit for the Future' consultation document (DHSS, 1998) the issue of front line health workers engaging with communities provides a significant contribution to problem-solving, and developing empowering approaches and partnerships with local communities.

Secretary of Garran and Croob Cross Community Association - Thoughts of a Local Community Member

The needs identified in the survey are without question relevant to the needs of the community, as seen from the eyes of a community member.

Co-operation at all levels is important from the point of view that 'toes don't get stood on'. You have a better chance of success, if all concerned are aiming at the one target. If all levels co-operate at the top, it is easier for those helping at the bottom, as lack of consistency between statutory agencies leads to those working within the community becoming disillusioned. A community development approach helps avoid this. Involving community members gives not only a sense of ownership, but also a sense of direction.

I feel a Rapid Participatory Appraisal is a faster method of doing a survey. This is important as it avoids initial interest being wasted. If you take the first step and can't take the second, you've wasted your time. Long, detailed surveys that include everyone may give more detailed information, but unless they lead to something, what's the point? - and in today's economic climate, cost is a big consideration. Money is often put to better use on follow-on measures.

I now wish to examine the contribution of the rural General Practice in facilitating community development. The contribution of the rural General Practice in facilitating community development is significant, in that it is able to promote our Association as it already has the trust of the entire community. Due to the religious divide, no community association would be able to establish itself in a church hall without being associated with that religion.

The GPs are perceived by the local community as honest brokers, and are excellent bridges for the crossing of community and statutory views and ideas, as they are not seen to be either members of the community by statutory agencies, or instruments of statutory authority by the community, but as being there to help.

Across a wide range of primary care disciplines, the ethos of community development has to be advantageous. It is a good vehicle to promote health and wellbeing, as it gives those at policy-making level the opportunity to have ideas filter up, instead of filtering down. Those dealing with practical problems at a grass roots level can have a lot to contribute in terms of weeding out waste.

While the Community Association would probably still have established itself eventually, the support of the Primary Care Team contributed significantly to the speed and development of the Association. We had on hand resources we could otherwise not obtain. Their assistance was vital in helping to maintain the momentum and give encouragement. While it may be impractical for urban GPs to become involved in something like this, certainly rural practices could learn a lot.

Another thought about community development from a community member's point of view, is that it legitimises the work of community volunteers. If I write to the DOE as myself, a community member, complaining about the lack of good road conditions, I am filed under 'complaining old bag'; but if I do it as Secretary of Garran and Croob Cross Community Association, they write back and attempt to do something about it. They then know that I probably have the support of the whole community. One complaining 'old bag' isn't hard to listen to; 3,924 are! Having a voice is good, but having a voice that is working with, rather than at various agencies, is better. Having the opportunity to gain access legitimately is very important.

Conclusion

The Ballyward experience was significant for a number of reasons: it highlighted the useful role that a community-orientated primary care approach can offer in setting health and social goals; it resulted in programmes linked to local needs and which supported local people's desires to take more responsibility for their own wellbeing. This is a recognised approach which has been used in other parts of the UK, eg Freeman et al (1997).

It demonstrated the value of rapid participatory appraisal as a means of engaging local people in defining their own health and social needs. It was imperative that the Rapid Participatory Appraisal was not left on its own, but followed up immediately by joint action from the C&BCHSST Community Worker and Banbridge District Council Economic Development Worker in facilitating the formation and resourcing of the local group. This maintained local impetus for action and capitalised on a Peace and Reconciliation Funding opportunity, which had to be accessed without delay.

The project encapsulated many of the classic principles of community development, including empowerment, local action, inter-agency work and multidisciplinary teamwork.

Given the current debate in the Health Service on future structures and on the role of primary care in Fit for the Future, set in the context of policies which are sympathetic to community development (eg Well Into 2000), the Ballyward experience provides an interesting insight into how community development and primary care can co-exist.

In conclusion, a community development approach can be used by primary care teams to address local health and social problems and create a dynamic for positive change.

References

Banbridge District Council (1994) Banbridge Local Economic Development Strategy 1994-1999, Banbridge District Council.

Department of Health (1991) The Patients' Charter, HMSO, London.

Department of Health & Social Services (1990) People First – Community Care in Northern Ireland, HMSO, Belfast.

Department of Health & Social Services (1996) Health and Wellbeing: Into the Next Millennium (Regional Strategy for Health and Social Wellbeing 1997-2002), HMSO, Belfast.

Department of Health & Social Services (1997) Well Into 2000, HMSO, Belfast.

Department of Health & Social Services (1998) Fit for the Future: A Consultation Document on the Government's Proposals for the Future of the Health and Personal Social Services in Northern Ireland, HMSO, Belfast.

Freeman, R, Gillan, S, Shearin, C and Pratt, J (1997) Community Development and Involvement in Primary Care: A Guide to Involving the Community in COPC, King's Fund, London.

Murray Scott, A (1995) 'Practice-based Health Needs Assessment: Use of Four Methods in a Small Neighbourhood', British Medical Journal, 310, pp 1443-1448.

Robson, B, Bradford, M and Deas, I (1994) Relative Deprivation in Northern Ireland, Policy Planning and Review Unit, Occasional Paper 28, Centre for Urban Policy Studies, Manchester University

Southern Health & Social Services Board (1995) The Annual Report of the Director of Public Health: Towards A Better Health 1995-1996, pp 24-26, SHSSB, Armagh.

6 Springs of Hope

Dr Philomena Horner

"Go to the people, live with them, learn from them, start with what they know, build with what they have. But with the best leaders, when the work is done, the task is accomplished, the people will say, 'We have done this ourselves'."

(Lao Tsu, China 700 BC quoted by Dunwoodie, 1994)

This early Chinese poem succinctly sums up a central value in community development - ie community empowerment.

Over the past thirty years, a range of community-based initiatives to meet local needs have developed across the UK. These range through community work, community action and community development. As popularly understood, however, 'community development' can mean anything from a local community campaigning for radical social change, to a tokenistic consultation exercise over decisions already taken outside the community. The present writer defines it in terms of 'enablement, support and empowerment', in line with the observation of Laughlin and Black, (1995) *"At the core of 'community development' as opposed to 'work with communities' is real involvement and empowerment of the community, sharing of power and decision-making, not just basing a worker in a locality."*

The Community Development and Health Network in Northern Ireland emphasises the central importance of social support networks. The working definition agreed by the Network (1994) is *"A Community Development approach to health is a process by which a community defines its own health needs to bring about change. The emphasis is on collective action to redress inequalities in health and in access to health care"*.

Community development is a process of empowering communities to struggle against the factors in their physical, social, or political environment which cause them to be excluded by their society. Laughlin and Black (1995) comment that: *".. 'social exclusion' is a useful phrase because it implies that people are being excluded by society as a whole - that their poverty is not their own fault but due to social structures and relationships"*. Those who are excluded by society are, by definition, deprived of the resources needed to participate fully in society. In other words, they are prevented from attaining a sense of wellbeing. Laughlin and Black (1995) quote the World Health Organisation (WHO) Constitution (1948), which defines health as:

> "...a state of complete physical, social and mental wellbeing and not merely the absence of disease or infirmity. The enjoyment of the highest attainable standard of health is one of the fundamental rights of every human being, without distinction of race, religion, political beliefs or economic or social conditions...".

Social exclusion is linked with poverty, which, for a number of reasons, takes its toll on mental wellbeing. Money and social status allow people freedom of choice and access to services. Low income and social deprivation, in contrast, are often linked with increased stress, lack of access to resources, and absence of social supports.

Such deprivation robs people of the sense of control over their own lives. Blackburn (1991) highlights this experience of powerlessness by reference to Fisher's (1984) theory of 'locus of control'. Fisher suggests that: "...those people who believe that they have some control over the source of stress may be less at risk of developing a sense of helplessness and depressive illnesses, than those who feel they have no control..." (Fisher, 1984, in Blackburn, 1991). Those who live on low income, dependent on social security benefits, have little opportunity to experience being in control. Often, such economic dependence is concomitant with stress, depression and feelings of low self-esteem.

Because low-income families often have little control over where they live, being allocated public authority housing as it becomes available, they are often isolated from their extended family and the friendship network which would cushion stress. Blackburn (1991), cites Curtice (1989), as commenting on the centrality of social networks: "Friends offer day to day help, act as confidantes, provide sociability, and are often valued for the empathy that comes from shared experience". Blackburn (1991) points out that this is particularly important for mothers of young, dependent children. Community development may begin with empowering individuals, raising levels of self-esteem and strengthening social networks. In the best practice, however, it needs to go on to strengthen community networks, build self-help activities and develop local leadership.

In coping with stress, Blackburn (1992) lists several factors which have been identified by low-income families as helpful or unhelpful. The helpful services included: an integrated approach; a co-ordinated response; services which are realistic and recognise the limitations created by poverty; partnership between families and workers in which families' experiences and contributions are recognised and valued; and services that are permanent, relevant and easy to use. Pat Tobin (1990) explains the link between personal development and community development as follows:

> *"Personal development is important and valuable work, since it is through this that women can identify the source of their oppression. However, if it is to be consistent with community work principles and ideals, it must go one step further and encourage women to take action on some of the issues that they have identified as being important to them."*

(Combat Poverty, 1990)

Laughlin and Black (1995) offer a useful model for working towards health and wellbeing at a community level. It assumes that wellbeing is reached via a number of hierarchical stages or outcomes (Fig 1). Activity focused only at any one level will not bring about health, and the balance of activities will depend on the characteristics of the specific community.

In a very deprived community where physical survival is in jeopardy, it will be necessary to begin work at the physical level - campaigning on issues of housing, employment and access to food. For other communities, the perceived need will be at another level. Laughlin and Black (1995), suggest that the ideal way is to respond to issues at a number of levels simultaneously. At every level, however, the aim is to empower local people to respond to these issues in their own way.

Sadan and Churchman (1997) define empowerment as: *"...change processes that are experienced through efforts to gain control over one's life, destiny and environment"*. They go on to comment that such processes: *"...would benefit from an empowering professional practice"*. Sadan and Churchman stress the importance of community empowerment by stating unequivocally that for professionals involved in a community, *"...we have eliminated the neutral option regarding empowerment"* (op cit). Not only must professionals be committed to facilitating the empowerment of local people, but they must also be critically self-aware and willing to change. *"A commitment to empowerment demands of professionals involved in community development the same critical consciousness regarding themselves and their work and the same ability to change and to adopt themselves to what is necessary"* (op cit, p13).

Alan Barr (1995) reiterates the view of Laughlin and Black that empowerment processes will take different forms in a variety of communities. He would not entirely agree with the assertion of the Community Development and Health Network (1994) that *"...the emphasis is on collective action to redress inequalities..."*. Barr takes the view that *"...oppression may manifest itself most forcibly in private worlds and effective action must engage with the real experience of people. Thus, for example, an empowerment strategy that wishes to address the economic and social disadvantages of women has to focus on the domestic economy and the home as much as the local economy and the community"* (op cit).

Barr (1995) quotes Conger (1989) in support of his proposition that those who wish collectively to empower must recognise the necessity of personal empowerment as its basis.

> *"We can think of empowerment as an act of strengthening an individual's beliefs in his or her sense of effectiveness... We know from psychology that individuals believe themselves powerful when they feel they can adequately cope with environmental demands... They feel powerless when they are unable to cope with these demands."*
>
> (Conger, 1989 in Barr, 1995)

The concept of community development is inextricably linked to that of personal empowerment. The question which confronts community development workers is how to balance the two in proportions which enhance individual and collective control of the environment. Sadan and Churchman (1997) have also identified a related question, ie the ability of professionals involved in community development to critically assess themselves and their role, and to adapt and change in response to community needs.

Springwell Centre will be presented here as a case study which illustrates many of the issues explored in this Chapter. Its rationale and modus operandi represent one response which the present writer regards as a replicable model of good practice. '

Springwell Centre

Springwell Centre's ambience demonstrates the practical application of an observation by C Wright Mills (1970): *"If people lack a sense of their effectiveness in their immediate relationships it will be difficult for them to engage with community needs. Agents of empowerment must therefore recognise the indivisibility of personal troubles and public issues"* (Mills, 1970, in Barr, 1995).

Springwell Centre came into being in February 1993, when a group of six lone parents came together for mutual support. As they reflected on their situation and their own needs, a number of factors emerged: a feeling of isolation, lack of a social support network, low self-esteem and lack of self-confidence. The group initially met on a weekly basis, but before long they recognised the benefits of meeting more frequently. Philomena Horner, a local teacher and community worker, had been involved with the group from the beginning. At their urging, she obtained the use of a building in Edward Street, Lurgan, and the Centre opened. The group sought funding and a series of information sessions and classes was set up. Stress management was an obvious need, and very early on the Centre approached the Craigavon and Banbridge Trust Community Mental Health and the Health Visiting Teams. Relaxation and stress management, and the Activate programme were among the first classes to be provided, and aspects of these have become regular features of the Springwell programme.

In the intervening five years, Springwell Centre has developed into a vibrant, thriving centre, providing a wide range of services - personal growth, family support, community development, adult education, counselling and family therapy.

A number of factors appear to have been crucial to this rapid expansion:

The early support of the Health Visiting Team was of major significance. They offered practical advice and encouragement, as well as giving input to groups on parenting skills and women's health issues. The Team made, and continue to make referrals, and their public support gave credibility to the Centre. Such co-operation illustrates partnership at its best. Since Springwell Centre was independent of the Trust, and there was no formal contract between the two bodies, each was able to contribute their strengths.

While the initiative should come from the grass roots, community groups like Springwell would be the first to agree that the professional community worker has a great deal to offer them. In the early phase of the project, as the women involved learned how to set up and develop a family centre, the Community Work Team was an important source of encouragement, as well as of practical networking and funding advice.

Springwell has directly addressed the contentious issue of the link between personal and community development. At one end of the spectrum, as Laughlin and Black (1995 point out, there is the school of thought which maintains that: "...*community development work involves working purely in and with communities to struggle against those organisations and policies which lead to them being disadvantaged and eventually to bring about radical social change*". At the other end of the spectrum is the view that personal empowerment is a prerequisite for community development. Blackburn (1991) cites Fisher (1984) as suggesting that beliefs about whether events are within one's control depend on previous life experiences. When people feel they have no control over the sources of stress in their life, not only are they likely to develop feelings of helplessness and depressive illness, but they are very unlikely to feel inclined or equipped to tackle systemic injustice.

Springwell Centre operates from the basis of the latter position. The staff are very aware of the effects of social exclusion, particularly on women. depression, anxiety, low self-esteem, lack of self-confidence and social isolation. The Centre personnel believe that the first approach to dealing with these is the provision of unconditional positive regard, encouragement and a social network. Blackburn (op cit), comments on the importance of the support of family and friends in providing a protective effect on mental health. She adds that in the absence of family, friends can be an important source of social support. Springwell seeks to provide such a social network, where women can benefit from the support of peers, who offer day to day help, empathy and social contact.

"*Having contact and help from someone who shares similar experiences has been shown to be a very valuable form of social support, especially for mothers with young, dependent children*" (Blackburn, op cit).

The progression from personal to community development is a slow one which cannot be forced. In Springwell Centre, it was four years before the women were able to begin to address issues of concern to them in their environment. During that time mutual support led to personal development courses. These sparked an interest in adult education, which in turn led to interest in contributing to the community. From the beginning, the women who use the Centre have been involved directly in programme planning, fundraising and mutual support. Women come to Springwell from a wide range of backgrounds and for a variety of reasons. Whatever form it takes, most feel a need for support through counselling, peer support or personal development. They come to Springwell on the advice of a friend, having read an advertisement or a notice, or through referral from a GP, Health Visitor or Social Worker. In 1996, a group undertook a course in Community Leadership, which imbued them with the confidence to be more proactive in managing the Centre and contributing to the design of the programme.

Partnership between Springwell Centre and Craigavon and Banbridge Trust grew gradually, and was formalised in 1997 with the setting up of the Parents' Support Programme, between the Young Persons' Project and Springwell Centre. The Support Programme is jointly delivered by personnel from the two organisations. In real terms, this partnership was not easily achieved. After the first six weeks' programme, the Trust's evaluation report implied that the Young Persons' Project had been the lead deliverer. Springwell Centre personnel were, not unnaturally, angry and disappointed, and it was after discussion of this difference of perception, that a partnership of mutual respect was established. It is a partnership which draws out the potential of each stakeholder. Trust personnel contribute financial and administrative strength. Springwell contribute premises with a supportive ambience, and staff who have developed considerable expertise in personal development and support for parents.

The development of this partnership between Craigavon and Banbridge Trust and a voluntary organisation demonstrates a point which Sadan and Churchman (1997) suggest is crucial to effective community development, ie the ability of the professionals involved to critically assess themselves and to adapt and change in response to community needs.

Springwell Centre is a vibrant example of a community development initiative which sprang from the grass roots, engaged the support of local community workers, and finally developed into a powerful and mutually-beneficial partnership between the community and the statutory sectors.

References

Barr, A (1995) 'Empowering Communities - Beyond Fashionable Rhetoric? Some Reflection on Scottish Experience', Community Development Journal, 30 2 April, pp 121-132.

Blackburn, C (1991) Poverty and Health: Working With Families, OUP, Milton Keynes.

Blackburn, C (1992) Improving Health and Welfare Work with Families in Poverty: A Handbook, OUP, Milton Keynes.

Combat Poverty (1990) Community Work in Ireland – Trends in the '80s, Options for the '90s, report of a conference organised by Combat Poverty at St Patrick's College, Maynooth, Combat Poverty Publishers, Dublin.

Conger, J A (1989) 'Leadership: The Art of Empowering Others', Academy of Management Executives, 3 1.

Curtice, L (1989) The First Year of Life, Maternity Alliance, London.

Dunwoodie, M (1994) 'The Challenge of Community Development', Celebrating Community Development and Health in Northern Ireland, conference report, Community Development and Health Network, Belfast.

Fisher, S (1984) Stress and Perceptions of Control, Lawrence Erlbaum Associates, London.

Fraser, H (1990) 'Integrated Approaches to Development', Community Work in Ireland, Combat Poverty, Dublin.

Jacobs, S and Popple, K (1994) Community Work in the '90s, Spokesman Press, Nottingham.

Laughlin, S and Black, D (eds) (1995) Tools for Change. A Public Health Trust Project, Public Health Alliance, Birmingham.

Mills, C W (1970) The Sociological Imagination, Pelican, London.

Rodgers, V (1994) Feminist Work and Community Education in Jacobs and Popple (1994).

Sadan, E and Churchman, A (1997) 'Process-focused and Product-focused Community Planning', Community Development Journal, 32 1.

Tobin, P (1990) Women in Community Work, pp 235-248 in Combat Poverty.

Whelan, M (1990) Training and Professionalisation in Community Work pp 145-163 in Combat Poverty.

7 Learning Together

A Personal Development Course for Traveller Women

Jacquie Kilfeather and Ruth Stewart

Introduction

This Chapter will focus on a personal development course for young Traveller women from Craigavon, Armagh and Newry. The course was organised by the Community Workers from Armagh Travellers' Support Committee and Craigavon Travellers' Support Committee. The rationale for the course was to engage Traveller women on issues relating to being a woman and being a Traveller. The original idea for the course came from two young Traveller women, one who lived in Craigavon and one in Armagh. These two young women had been friends for years and had previously taken part in a course together. This course was facilitated by Craigavon Travellers' Support Committee's Community Worker and an external facilitator.

Significant members of the Travelling community reside in all these locations (and additionally at Coalisland), within the parameters of the Southern Health & Social Services Board and Southern Education & Library Board. The young women from Newry were all from St Christopher's Park, where thirty families reside on a permanent basis on a site which is designed with twenty pitches, including utility buildings with toilet, shower, kitchen and storage space. In all of the above-mentioned areas some Traveller families also reside in Housing Executive accommodation.

The situation is somewhat different in Armagh and Craigavon, where there is a complete absence of serviced site provision. This means that nomadic families are forced to wait on unserviced roadside sites, without access to clean water, electricity, sanitation, refuse collection and many other facilities which members of the settled community take for granted. For those families who live on serviced or on unserviced halting sites the situation is comparable. Low self-esteem tends to co-exist with appalling living conditions. Some of the practical consequences arising from this are high levels of tension between Traveller and settled people; racist attacks and discrimination; harassment and eviction; a lack of access to mainstream services, for example, health and education and a lack of basic amenities, for example, clean water, sanitation, refuse collection. These are all realities of life for the young women who attended the personal development course in Chrysalis Women's Centre in Craigavon.

Definition of Terms

Traveller

When the term 'Traveller' is used in this study, it is taken to mean members of the distinct ethnic minority group of that name. The Traveller communities in Northern Ireland form a distinct and separate ethnic group by virtue of fulfilling the recognised criteria, including a long, shared history and their own cultural tradition.[1] In addition, a common geographical origin; descent from a small number of common ancestors; a common language; a common religion; and that they are characteristically a minority or oppressed group within a larger community, are also relevant characteristics. Furthermore, the term 'Traveller' refers to the membership of this group, and not just to the distinction between a nomadic and settled lifestyle.

Prejudice and Racism

Definitions of 'prejudice' include the following: to pre-judge a person, group or situation; a viewpoint which is biased and has been formed prior to an encounter; an attitude which colours our view of the world; a conscious or unconscious aspect of everyone's make-up. However, prejudice is not racism. 'Racism' is a specific form of discrimination. Power relations are crucial to racism. Power legitimises the prejudice to produce the equation: prejudice and power equals racism.

Racism is a particular form of discrimination, a dominant form of which is based upon the abuse of skin colour. Other forms of racism are based upon real or imagined physical or cultural difference. Anti-Traveller racism is based on the sedentary/nomadic divide. Racism is something that all members of the dominant group are socialised into. Racism can be overt or covert, conscious or unconscious, and occurs at both an individual and an institutional level. Racism is best identified in terms of the outcomes generated for a particular group, for example, Travellers.

---

[1] House of Lords, Mandela vs Lee 1983

Community Development

The Community Development Review Group (1993) gave the following broad definition of Community Development :

> *"Community Development in Northern Ireland is a process which embraces community action, community service, community work and other community endeavour - whether geographical or issue-based - with emphasis towards the disadvantaged, impoverished and powerless within society. Its values include participation, empowerment and self-help. And while it is essentially about collective action, it helps to realise the potential of both individuals and groups within communities. In the interest of developing this potential, community development challenges prejudice, sectarianism and the unequal distribution of resources, both in terms of financial resources and access to skills and knowledge. Community development is the process which underpins collectivist approaches to education, economic development and the delivery of services in a situation in Northern Ireland where, for various reasons, there have been few opportunities for communities to participate in the democratic process."*

The course employed community development methodologies in working with Traveller women. The model used was based on the work of Paulo Friere (in Training for Transformation, Hope et al, 1992) where members of a particular community are engaged in animation work with a facilitator. The work begins at a point relevant to the members of the community (using something they can easily relate to) and considers where they are at, in comparison with where they would like to be. The purpose of this process is to raise the level of consciousness of participants in relation to their own life circumstances. It is important in work with Travellers that materials used do not rely on literacy skills. It should be clear at this point that the course was facilitated by non-Travellers and that this chapter is written by settled women, and consequently reflects their perspective.

It was considered important to employ community development methods in a personal development course, as any form of collective action is, essentially, undertaken by groups of individuals. Therefore, logically, consciousness-raising needs to begin on an individual basis by recognising the current life circumstances of the participants.

Course Development

The course was developed over a period of approximately eight weeks using the following process.

Meetings were convened with two staff members from Belfast Travellers' Education and Development Group and Pavee Point, Dublin, both of whom had previously held courses for Traveller women. The experiences of these agencies were discussed and resource materials were reviewed. Discussions were then held with Traveller women who were residing in Armagh and Craigavon, in their own trailers or houses. This was followed by a Christmas lunch when twelve Traveller women took part in a discussion about the course, prior to the meal being served. When the actual design of the course began, the facilitators called upon two colleagues (with experience of Traveller work and adult education) and two Traveller women to have an input.

Course Aims

The course aims came directly from the process of developing the course, as previously described These course aims are listed below

1. To develop among participants a conscious knowledge and understanding of Traveller history and culture.

2. To develop among participants a greater sense of self-awareness and the skills, as well as the confidence, to address the issues affecting their lives in a positive and constructive manner.

3. To explore the issue of gender and the role of women in the Traveller community and Irish society, in a way which is as liberating as possible for the participants

4. To employ creative and artistic methods to celebrate being a Traveller and being a woman.

Getting Started

Week One - Introductions

Nine women attended the initial class for this personal development course. Of these nine women, eight were single while only one was married. The married woman was slightly older than the other participants and had a number of children. She participated in the first session but seemed to distance herself from the rest of the group and did not return again. The remainder of the women ranged in age from seventeen to early twenties. It should have been noted by the facilitators at an earlier stage that in the Traveller community, women who are married with children, have a significantly different status and role from that of young, single women. Consequently, it was an unrealistic expectation that a married woman remain as part of this group.

The young women's aspirations for the course were that it would provide some space for themselves as individuals, away from their family responsibilities, where they would have an opportunity to meet with their friends for a chat. It was seen as an opportunity by the young women to discuss issues that they considered important, in a safe environment and away from parental pressures. Based on this, the objectives for each session were set.

The objectives for the first session were: to promote participants' ownership of the course; to build relationships between group members; to allow group members to explore their feelings, their hopes and their fears; and to encourage group decision-making.

It was apparent from both verbal and non-verbal behaviour that the participants were not at ease at the outset of the session; however, this seemed to gradually abate as the morning progressed. The following ground rules were discussed and agreed upon - punctuality/timekeeping, confidentiality, responsibility for attendance and participation, respect for self and others, honesty/trust and openness/setting boundaries.

Of the nine participants, only two had limited literacy and numeracy skills. Consequently, a number of activities which promoted group discussion, but did not require literacy skills, were used during the session. The women were reluctant to share with each other, for example, in relation to their hopes and fears, but eagerly debated the destination and activity for the Week Six outing. All the women indicated that they had enjoyed the session when asked to evaluate it at the conclusion.

Week Two - Beauty and Skin-Care

The objectives for this session were: to introduce basic principles of skin-care, cleansing, toning and moisturising; to introduce techniques of cosmetic make-up. Ten women attended this skin-care and make-up demonstration by Clinique skin consultants. For all of these young women this would have been a new experience. The model of listening to talks and presentations is one frequently used in courses with the settled community, however this did not translate particularly well in working with Travellers. Most of the women were attentive throughout the demonstration, but several were disruptive. Consequently, the demonstration was shortened by the skin consultant, who expressed frustration. It should be recognised that the settled model of presentations required further refinement in this situation; for example, a more practically-based session would have been more appropriate. Most of these young women would have had a very limited experience of formal education, and therefore they have less experience of the structures of classes compared with settled people.

Who Am I?

The session entitled "Who am I?" took place over two weeks, with the women from Newry attending on one occasion and the women from Armagh/Craigavon attending on the other. This did not happen by design, but simply reflected the attendance pattern in the group. The objectives of this session were to work with various materials using collage as a means of expression, and to give participants space to look at their lives and to learn more about themselves.

It was hoped that during this session the women would have an opportunity to look at their lives and begin to develop a self-awareness about who they are as individuals, and collectively as a group. The purpose of self-disclosure in any group is to break down the barriers between participants, reduce the sense of isolation that individuals may be experiencing and promote a trusting, supportive atmosphere. It also provides an opportunity for people to become aware of their feelings in a positive atmosphere.

The aspects of their lives that the women were asked to include in the collage were their current roles and responsibilities; what is important to them (their values); what makes them feel content and/or happy; their interests, activities or hobbies and their present lifestyle.

The exercise stimulated lively discussion and creativity amongst the participants. Not all the women took the exercise seriously; however, they all appeared to enjoy the opportunity for self-expression. The informal setting also seemed to promote an atmosphere of openness and sharing. The collages were all very colourful, with a creative use of the craft materials provided.

When the collages were completed, the women were asked to share the contents of their own collage with the rest of the group as a means of encouraging self disclosure. All the women willingly participated in this aspect of the session. Most of the collages focused on material items, for example, cars, trailers and other possessions. Six of the ten women who participated in the session lived in a trailer, and all of the women, with only one exception, stated they would prefer to live in a trailer, rather than a house.

Life Maps

The following objectives were set for this session: to give participants a chance to think about the effect which their past has on their present situation; and to use art and creativity to help participants identify areas for change in their lives.

The format of this session was altered slightly by the facilitators to take the form of an open discussion about the women's past and present circumstances and to link the two, so that participants could, if they wished, begin to identify areas for change. Participants were asked to think about their lives, past and present, and were encouraged to identify things they would like to change as individuals and collectively.

All the women adhered to traditional rules regarding their behaviour, responsibilities and activities; for example, the women were from families where arranged marriages were the norm and marriage was regarded as the most important event in a woman's life. The women all came from large families and had significant responsibilities for the care of siblings. This impacted on their ability to have time for themselves. All the women expressed a desire to have more freedom to socialise or visit places of interest to them. Currently, unstructured social interaction formed the main leisure activity for all the women. A minority of the women specifically expressed an interest in developing roles for themselves outside the home. There was a strongly expressed preference to be nomadic.

The majority of the women had experienced discriminatory treatment by the settled community, for example, being refused service in shops. Obviously, the women wanted to be able to go into a shop and be served just the same as any one else would. All of the women had extremely negative memories of their experience of school and the discrimination they had experienced there; nevertheless, they saw education as important and supported their younger siblings to attend school and learn.

Finally, in this session the women were asked if there was anything they might like to change or achieve in the future, ie "Where am I/we?" – "Where do I/we want to go?" – "How do I/we get there?".

In spite of some of the desires the participants had expressed earlier in the discussion, this part of the session met with no response, except for one woman stating: *"We don't want anything different - we're all very happy."*

Endings and Reflection

Due to two bereavements in the Travelling Community, the women were not available to attend sessions during two subsequent weeks. On the third week, none of the women attended the session, and despite enquiries, no explanations were provided for non-attendance. The facilitators met and decided that in view of the lack of attendance from the participants, the course should be officially discontinued. The course ran for five of the planned ten weeks.

Much thought and energy had been put into structuring and presenting the course in an appropriate manner. A comfortable meeting room had been provided at the Chrysalis Women's Centre, and a positive atmosphere was promoted within the group. Although the women seemed to enjoy the opportunity to come together to talk, there were barriers to the learning process, the group process and the achievement of objectives. While literacy limitations did impact, there also appeared to be cultural features and group dynamics which prevented full commitment, attendance and participation. In general, the agreed ground rules were not adhered to. However, the concept of ground rules was unfamiliar to the course participants, as was the process of group work. This was not fully appreciated by the course facilitators.

Attendance at the sessions was interrupted by parental control, peer pressure, bereavements and a family conflict on site. Constructive participation and group progress were hindered by seemingly short attention spans of participants, disruptive behaviour within the group, peer pressures, competitive attitudes between the women from the different sites (and from different extended families), and a difficulty on the part of participants to self-disclose. Again the facilitators brought their own perspectives to these exercises. As settled people, they did not fully appreciate that self-disclosure is an alien concept within Traveller culture. It is not within the Traveller culture for individuals to express their feelings. Therefore, it was an unrealistic goal to expect the young women, after a few sessions, to engage in this exercise in a meaningful way. It is only after a sustained, nurturing process and the build-up of trust, that this outcome could be considered appropriate.

Attempts to promote collective awareness within the group as a means to appreciating and celebrating Traveller culture, were met with significant resistance. The response was defensive, giving the impression that the women felt their culture was being threatened or challenged, rather than respected. This was undoubtedly informed by the women's past experience of being exposed to prejudice and discrimination from settled people. It was difficult for the settled facilitators to build up an appropriate relationship with the young women. It is now our experience that Travellers respond much more positively and openly to Traveller facilitators.

The women displayed little interest in learning about health issues or the links between lifestyle and health status. The women tended to equate health with basic survival, which is understandable in view of their environmental living conditions. (See Chapter 8 on Travellers' health.)

Funding Mechanism

The course was funded through the Community Arts Programme of the Northern Ireland Voluntary Trust, and by Craigavon Travellers' Support Committee. An assessment interview was held which was attended by one of the course participants. The facilitators viewed this as a major step forward, since it was the first occasion when a young Traveller had taken part in such a process. This was a learning experience for both the Assessment Officer (who had never met a Traveller before) and the young Traveller woman, who had no understanding of the various components of the process necessary for a course to move to the point of delivery. Traditionally, funding for any course has been dependent on having sufficient numbers enrolled. It is not appropriate to apply this formula to working with Travellers, due to the amount of intensive individual support required.

Evaluation

At the conclusion of each session, a short verbal evaluation was undertaken. During the evaluation the following questions were asked and the answers noted by the facilitators:-

- What did you learn from the session?
- What did you find most interesting about the session?
- What did you dislike about the session?
- What would you change about the session?

During the discussion of each evaluation question, the participants shared their thoughts and feelings about the content of the session. The feedback received from these exercises informed the ongoing development of the course, and has also contributed significantly to future practice.

Lessons Learnt

The lessons learnt on community development/personal development work with Travellers and the recommendations, are based upon the knowledge and insights gained by the two facilitators through the five sessions undertaken with this small group of Traveller women.

Need for Awareness and a Culturally Sensitive Approach

Developing trust between participants and facilitators is essential to any course, but particularly so when different traditions are represented. An ethnically-sensitive approach is required to ensure that discussions and activities are not viewed as threatening to the traditions or status quo of the Traveller community. Increased awareness and appreciation amongst the Traveller community of their own history and traditions would enhance their cultural identity and collective sense of worth. To enhance the opportunities for awareness and learning, it would be preferable that activities be led by Traveller facilitators. It should also be recognised that the Traveller community is organised around extended family groups. Therefore, it is important that this informs any work undertaken.

Need to Develop Self-Esteem

Acquiring self-esteem and building self-confidence is essential for promoting any form of empowerment, which might lead to collective action and effecting change in matters such as discrimination and conflict. While personal development and community development methodologies provide a useful framework for promoting self-esteem, the insights of this course would indicate that members of the Traveller community may benefit more from informal learning opportunities. This could involve anything from individual learning to participation in group activities or workshops; however, it is essential that all opportunities are relevant to the experiences, interests, or needs of the participants to ensure ongoing commitment. Skills-based courses will only be successful and beneficial if they are designed in a way that is applicable to Travellers' life circumstances.

In order to increase self-esteem, Travellers need to affirm themselves and be affirmed in ways that are meaningful to them. It is essential to acknowledge and build upon their achievements, strengths, and skills. Learning pathways should be established by building on prior experiences, on transferable skills, and identifying areas where change is either desired or required.

With specific reference to Traveller women, it should be recognised that childcare is a major role expectation, and consequently, the formation of carers groups and pre-school playgroups are essential elements of development. Traveller women's groups should also be encouraged to explore gender issues and their role within the Traveller community. Additionally, it would be helpful to view the traditional role of Traveller women in a broader context, so they can validate themselves and recognise that they share some of the same challenges and frustrations of women in mainstream society.

It must be acknowledged that developments along these lines would necessitate change if they were to be implemented, and any form of change may be regarded as threatening to the Traveller family and community network. Such changes must be seen as constructive, rather than negative and detrimental. In addition, interaction with settled people is to be recommended to break down the barriers which make Travellers feel inferior, marginalised and discriminated against. Travellers should be encouraged to take opportunities, in a safe environment, to share experiences, information and insights to promote a positive ethos and identity. It is hoped that this would, in time, contribute to an atmosphere of mutual understanding, equality and respect for other traditions.

Need for Enhanced Literacy Skills

It must be acknowledged that improvements in literacy skills would be advantageous for a whole range of reasons, including improved communication skills, increased skills and capacity and the encouragement of development. It is, however, imperative to take cognisance of the value of the oral tradition in Traveller culture, and incorporate it into the design of any method of learning.

Summary

The main lessons learnt that will inform the future practice of Craigavon Travellers' Support Committee in personal development and community development work, are the need for Traveller facilitators; intensive work within extended family groups, and delivery mechanisms appropriate to Traveller culture.

References

Combat Poverty Agency (1994) Creating a Difference, Report of the Creative Activity for Everyone Community Arts Pilot Programme 1993 - 1994, Combat Poverty Agency, Dublin.

Community Development Review Group (1991) Community Development in Northern Ireland: Perspectives for the Future, Community Development Review Group, Belfast.

Friere, P in Hope, A and Timmel, S (1992) Training for Transformation. A Handbook for Community Workers, Mambo Press, Zimbabwe.

Kelly-Lyth, M (1995) A Historical and Contemporary Analysis of Aboriginal Australians Including a Comparison with Travellers in Northern Ireland, Northern Ireland Council for Travelling People, Belfast.

Noonan, P (1994) Travelling People in West Belfast, Save the Children Fund, Belfast.

Pavee Point, (1995) Traveller Ways, Traveller Words, Pavee Point Publications, Dublin.

Pavee Point, (1996) A Heritage Ahead, Cultural Action and Travellers, Pavee Point Publications, Dublin.

8 Making Health Services Accessible to Travellers

Joan Green

The Traveller community is an ethnic group whose culture is identified by a history dating back to the 12th Century. They share customs and traditions – nomadism, language, marrying within their own society and complementary systems of healing. The Traveller community is recognised under the Race Relations (Northern Ireland) Order 1997 as an ethnic minority group. They experience difficulties accessing many services, in particular primary health care.

As a Health Visitor working with the Traveller community within the Craigavon area and supported by Craigavon Travellers' Support Committee, I act as an advocate for this vulnerable group, highlighting the many inequalities which they suffer and which are so apparent. The approach taken in the work uses the four principles of health visiting: the search for health needs; the stimulation of an awareness of health needs; the influence on policies affecting health; the facilitation of health-enhancing activities. Applying the four Health Visiting Principles, and in partnership with the Traveller community, I aim to identify the impact of their environment, lifestyle and nomadism on their health and social wellbeing. I include a profile of the health visiting input and case studies to demonstrate the inequalities of health experienced by them.

The Traveller community in the Craigavon area live on unapproved sites, which in effect makes them trespassers and inevitably leads to eviction. This fact brings uncertainty and trauma, and makes the provision of health care difficult and of low priority to them. The sites are environmentally unsafe and lack basic amenities such as sanitation, clean running water, refuse collection and electricity - amenities the settled population take for granted. These circumstances are associated with a variety of problems: poor living conditions; increased morbidity; a higher rate of accidents; social isolation and exclusion; marginalisation and prejudice against the Travellers.

Craigavon Travellers' Support Committee

This support group for Travellers was formed in the late 1980s. Its membership included personnel from the voluntary and statutory sectors and interested members of the public. The present Committee includes representation from: Craigavon and Banbridge Community Health & Social Services Trust; Craigavon Borough Council; TRUST (Towards Respect and Understanding Community Relations); Save the Children; Southern Education & Library Board; Moylinn House CDSSA (Community Development Support Services Agency) and the Group's Community Worker. It would be an asset to have a member of the Traveller community on this Committee; however, this has proved difficult to achieve, but is a hope for the future.

The aim of the Support Committee is to improve the quality of life for Travellers in the Craigavon area. Its objectives include: adopting a community development approach which will enable Travellers to articulate their needs and to support them in taking steps to ensure that their needs are met; engaging the range of statutory and voluntary bodies in order to ensure the provision of appropriate, culturally-sensitive services; to highlight the problems arising from the lack of recognition/acceptance of Travellers as an ethnic group and the consequences of this in terms of experiencing racism; to help alleviate prejudice and misunderstanding, so enhancing community co-operation and mutual support.

The work of the Craigavon Travellers' Support Committee includes promoting partnerships to advance levels of co-operation between the Project, Travellers, the voluntary and statutory sectors – to identify and address health and social needs of Travellers in the Craigavon area.

The focus of this chapter is on health – to increase the health of the Traveller population by adopting a community development approach which will forge new partnerships and health alliances between health professionals, the Travellers and the Project.

Meeting the Support Committee's aims and objectives is a very slow process hampered by bureaucracy, local opinions and the nomadic lifestyle of the Travellers. However, it has been possible to build a network of contacts with health visitors, other professionals and workers in the voluntary sector in areas throughout Northern Ireland, which has brought about some continuity of care and unity of purpose.

A health survey of the Traveller population in Northern Ireland shows the difficulty of the task:-
18% of Travellers are under 5 years of age - compared to 8% in the settled community.

53% of Travellers are under 17.

10% of Travellers are over 40.

1% live over the age of 65 - compared to 13% in the settled community.

Infant mortality rates are 3 times greater than in the settled community.

Physical disability is 3 times greater than in the settled community.

There are higher levels of chronic illness than in the settled community.

Research has also demonstrated that Travellers in Northern Ireland have poorer health than the most disadvantaged groups in the settled community, and do not as yet compare with the concept of health as defined by the World Health Organisation as *"A state of complete physical, mental and social wellbeing, not merely the absence of disease or infirmity"* (WHO, 1946).

Work Identified and Carried Out by the Health Visitor

It has been necessary to spend time within the Traveller community to study their lifestyle, hear their views and assess their needs, in order to identify ways in which these needs can be addressed in partnership with the Travellers and their Community Worker from the Craigavon Travellers' Support Committee. Over the past five years, as the Health Visitor nominated to work within this community, I have, where possible, visited new families moving into the Craigavon area within a week of their arrival. I may be notified initially by the Community Worker or by another member of Craigavon Travellers' Support Committee, but more often the notification comes by telephone from one of the members of the Health Centre staff who have observed the caravans parked at the side of the road.

As a Health Visitor visiting these Traveller families, I have become a known name and have built a relationship of trust within their community. This is important for a professional from the settled community to be able to work effectively with Travellers.

Initially, I visited the sites to assess the needs of the children under five, namely: their general health, immunisation status and developmental progress. I also identify antenatal women, referring them on to the midwifery team, who support and advise these women throughout pregnancy and ensure antenatal appointments at the hospital are kept.

Visits are made to postnatal mothers and their babies on the 10th – 12th day following delivery; to give support, advice, continue their postnatal care, examine the babies, address issues such as childcare and management, which includes information on parenting, preparation of feeds and sterilisation of feeding equipment, maintaining freedom of infection and information on the immunisation programme and developmental assessments. Through this service given to mothers and their young children, many other issues have been identified, which relate to all ages in the community. These issues have diversified and expanded the role of the Health Visitor.

To address the health needs of the Travellers, it is necessary to understand the culture and attitudes of Travellers towards their health. Whilst interviewing Travellers for her report 'The Health of Travellers' (1993), Dr Pauline Ginnety's findings include such statements from Travellers as: *"Traveller children are exposed to the cold...makes them stronger". "You look around you, it's only the very old who get very, very sick."*

Dr Ginnety points out that:

> *"Women's health is recognised as generally being less good than men's, although men are aware of the lower life expectancy rates, both men and women perceive women's health to be affected by child-bearing, but the effects of unremitting work and worry about their families tends to be recognised by women alone."*

Health Issues Identified by Travellers in the Craigavon Area

A major issue with Travellers who are using illegal sites is the inability to register with a GP except on a temporary basis; this excludes them from primary health care, assessment and screening programmes. However, some GPs in the area do treat Travellers who are ill and arrange consultations for antenatal and postnatal mothers and their babies on a temporary residence basis. The fact is:

"There is little incentive for GPs to register Travellers who will not enhance the performance targets of the practice. Immunisation programmes and a range of other preventive measures count towards targets – and therefore payments. Travellers, because of transience or attitudes towards these services, often do not complete these programmes." Derek Howes (1997)

Women's Health

The health of Traveller women is affected by a number of issues. Many young women within their own community expect to have many pregnancies – not all these pregnancies will have a positive outcome. They receive no pre-conceptional care or advice. There is little or no antenatal care. Women may see a midwife for the first time in the last few weeks of pregnancy and subsequently book into the hospital very late. They frequently have inadequate postnatal care. There is no breast screening and little cervical screening - those who do have this test may not get the result, as they have no postal address or they move on. Depression is common, and it may be treated in a very ad hoc way. Women have the sole responsibility for children's health and tend to put the health of the children before their own. They often suffer severe distress caused by frequent eviction from sites, and domestic violence is an issue. Many women smoke – starting in their early teens. In discussion with Traveller women, I found that they were easily embarrassed and found it difficult to talk about their own bodies. Self-examination procedures are out of the question, related to a lack of privacy.

Men's Health

Men consider themselves to be 'fit and healthy' and are really not interested in talking about health - considering it a woman's territory. They are aware of the statistics, and feel men in their late fifties are old and get sick and die early. Not unlike the settled community, many Traveller men smoke, use alcohol and have poor knowledge of health check screening. As with many men in the settled community, they do not usually have health checks and seek medical attention as a last resort. Issues associated with their lifestyle, such as eviction, result in stress.

Children's Health

The health of the children takes priority with the women – it is their custom to overfeed babies and wean to solid food early on the assumption that 'a fat baby is a healthy baby'. Very few Traveller women breastfeed, mainly due to a lack of privacy.

Children are not immunised early and developmental assessments are delayed. The incidence of accidents, both in the home and outside, is higher than average. There are frequent visits to the Accident/Emergency Unit with minor illnesses or injury.

Children are exposed to passive smoking. There is a higher incidence of skin disease, upper respiratory tract infections, otitis media, gastro-enteritis, chest infections, poor dental health and lack of treatment. The needs of children with disabilities are not met, often follow-up appointments are not kept, or the child is seen at many hospitals throughout Northern Ireland and the Republic of Ireland.

Other Health Issues Relating to the Whole Community :

Travellers tend to be isolated, with little contact with the settled community, there are very few systems to track their health progress. Consequently, there is a lack of continuity of care, treatment/medication is not completed and medicines may be incorrectly stored. The preferred method of treatment is antibiotics. Skin diseases, namely scabies and impetigo, are common. Travellers may not receive medical appointments due to difficulties with the postal delivery service. There is often anxiety following a hospital or GP consultation - due to a lack of understanding and communication. The use of cures, herbal treatment and prayers is part of their custom. This may (for the adult Traveller) mean that conventional diagnosis and treatment is left as a last resort, and this may have serious consequences.

Literacy and Communication

Many Travellers are not able to read health education literature. If they do receive appointments for the hospital by post, there may not be someone readily available to read the letter, subsequently the appointment is not kept. Over the past four years, parent-held child records have been issued to the parents of children under the age of four. These are quite 'wordy' documents, but even so they are welcomed by mothers, as they appreciate that other professionals can follow their children's progress. These records are designed not only to document developmental progress, but to be a complete record of the child's health. Unlike the mother from the settled community, Traveller mothers cannot easily check the child's progress for themselves. However, GPs and hospital personnel often do not use them: many mothers within the settled community have tried to present the records to hospital staff with little or no success. Travellers have difficulty communicating with reception staff, both in doctors' surgeries and in hospitals. It is important for such staff to remember that not everyone can read notices and therefore may need to ask very basic questions.

The settled community are very much organised by time: Travellers are not. Most homes do not have a clock, women do not wear watches; so difficulties arise keeping appointments, which can cause frustration for those offering a service.

Considering these factors, people who make any attempt to make changes to improve the health of the Travellers face a difficult task. Where possible, direct intervention, advice, support and counselling from health professionals is taking place: the difference between this and working within the settled community is the lack of continuity of care.

By identifying all these issues and taking into account customs, practices and attitudes, it is seen that many of them could be addressed by appropriate intervention and health education at a local level. However, there are many environmental and social issues, such as conditions on sites and illiteracy, which impinge on health. Here change is not possible until policy-makers address the wider needs of Travellers, including their living environment and education. It is also necessary for professionals working with Travellers to find ways of communicating with and consulting them, hearing their views and acted on their identified needs.

Current Practice in Health Visiting With the Travellers

When a new family moves into the Craigavon area, a needs assessment of the family takes place. Where possible, this is followed by making contact with professionals in the area they have moved from; often this is difficult and past history may not be available. This being the case, outstanding and current assessments are carried out, and if a child is not reaching recognised developmental milestones, a referral is made to the appropriate agencies. One particular area presenting difficulties is assessing speech and language, as Travellers have a dialect and language of their own which is mixed with English. However, with parental co-operation and guidance, and if no concerns are expressed, the assessment can be passed as satisfactory. If a problem is identified, a referral to the Speech and Language Department will be made, but due to this Department's waiting list, and the inability of Travellers to continue therapy as they move on – the child often goes untreated.

Upon determination of the immunisation status of the children and where a child has not had any immunisations, arrangements are made for that child to be examined by a GP, and the first immunisation is given within the surgery environment; subsequently immunisations are given on the transit site. It may take a year to eighteen months to complete the primary immunisation programme, but there have been improvements in uptake, as gradually the importance of immunisation and the fears surrounding it have been addressed. Now most families with children under sixteen who have returned to the area have completed the programme.

Antenatal Care – although women want to be assured that their baby is 'alright', their custom is not to seek antenatal care until after the fifth month of pregnancy. In reality, Traveller women frequently arrive in Craigavon 32-39 weeks' pregnant, having had little or no antenatal care, and not being booked into a hospital. This situation is treated urgently and the Midwifery Team is alerted, the mother is assessed and subsequently booked into Craigavon Area Hospital, midwifery is continued through to the postnatal period and then transferred to the Health Visitor.

As pregnancy tends to be foremost in a young married couple's mind, if this does not occur it can ultimately cause marital disharmony. It is often perceived as 'the woman's fault' and this may result in her depression. Referral is often made to the family planning clinic where the woman can be advised and examined to rule out any obvious problem. Counselling these women and their husbands, when they make themselves available, takes time. If the family moves on, the situation may remain unresolved, with consequent unhappiness for those concerned.

Mental Health – Depression
A general depression can be seen as part of life, related to lack of basic facilities, stress of eviction, shortage of money, being unable to make oneself understood.

Post-natal depression – when it occurs, is usually seen three months following birth. This often goes untreated and is misunderstood by the family, who may feel the mother is rejecting her baby. The Health Visitor's discussions with Travellers, and information given to them about the causes of postnatal depression, have brought much-needed understanding to these women and their families.

Thirdly, there is depression associated with menopause – one must realise that in the Traveller community, a woman's role is to be a wife and mother. As the childbearing years come to an end, there may be distress due to lack of understanding. I have counselled several women and referred them to a GP for hormone replacement therapy, if appropriate.

Case History One

One Traveller woman felt she was going to die, she cried often every day, spent a lot of time alone in the caravan with depression, mood swings, irregular periods, haemorrhaging, sweating, unable to sleep. Her children were very worried – *"...she must be very ill - she must have cancer...".* Fortunately, this family stayed in the area for about three months - time for health education and counselling to take place. The mother was referred to the family planning clinic for examination and reassurance, and HRT treatment commenced. Three months later this lady had a totally changed outlook. The daughters understood the changes in the lifecycle of a woman, and her son was happy to have his 'mother back'. The family moved on.

Diabetes

In the course of my work over the years I have seen three adult diabetics – two of whom were insulin-dependent, the other diet-controlled - each of these people had different diet sheets, booklets and other information from various hospitals, which is confusing for persons with low literacy skills – all three were unstabilised. In two cases, this was rectified simply by explaining their diet and adjusting it according to the family routine.

Case History Two

A Traveller man aged sixty-five, a widower, living with his two daughters. This gentleman had been taken in a coma to Accident & Emergency Departments in hospitals in Northern Ireland and the Republic of Ireland many times in the previous year. When I saw him, his blood sugar was raised and urine analysis showed sugar and acetone. He complained constantly of pains in his limbs, headaches, blurred vision and nausea. He was very concerned about his health, he felt out of control and his daughters felt powerless to help him, yet he refused to see a doctor. I discussed the management of diabetes with the whole family, offering them advice and support. They produced three diet books which they could neither read or understand. It became obvious through discussion that his diet was a problem. As he travelled around he had no continued health care, nor had he been able to keep appointments at Diabetic Clinics. In partnership with him, we rearranged his diet plan using graphics, along with a simple graph to record sugar levels in blood and urine, which made controlling his diabetes and insulin requirement easier. Within three weeks he was stabilised and felt much better. A follow-up appointment at the Royal Victoria Hospital in Belfast was made but my client failed to attend. Six months later I met up with the family again and he had had no further hypo- or hyperglycaemic attacks. He, like many other chronically ill Travellers, had little or no continuity of care or medical records, and this leads to high morbidity.

Learning/Physical Disability

The adolescent with a learning or physical disability is looked after by the extended family, but they do not have access to services, facilities or equipment. A boy aged sixteen years had a broken caliper for nine months which robbed him of his mobility; his caliper was being held together by wire and insulating tape. An arrangement was made for him to attend Musgrave Park Hospital where his caliper was overhauled, repaired and refitted. It was humbling to see someone so grateful for a service that we take for granted.

Care in the Sun

In the hot summer of 1995, a number of Traveller children were seen to be very sunburnt, several were admitted to Craigavon Area Hospital with second degree burns and/or dehydration. Traveller parents had not got the health education message that sun damages the skin and increases the risk of melanoma – their belief is that sun toughens the skin and makes the child healthy. I talked to family groups, giving them the relevant information - encouraging the use of sunscreen/block, the wearing of tee shirts and hats - this was reinforced by the Community Worker and myself each time we visited the site - we received a very positive reaction in the community.

Conclusion

The cornerstone of the inequalities suffered by Travellers continues to be racism and the lack of facilities that ensues. Monies have been granted from the National Lottery to the Craigavon Travellers' Support Committee to provide a six pitch transit site. An application to the Council Planning Department is currently the subject of a Public Inquiry. This site would have basic amenities such as electricity, water, sanitation and refuse collection. The prospect of a serviced site and families staying longer will present a challenge to provide services in education and health. Working with Traveller families to improve their health and social wellbeing, by health education and empowering them to access primary health care, will make a difference to their level of health.

As a Health Visitor with five years of experience working with nomadic Travellers in the Craigavon area, and operating without readily available medical support, I have been a constant advocate for them, battling for Travellers' rights. The fact is, Travellers are recognised as an ethnic minority group under the Race Relations (Northern Ireland) Order 1997, making it unlawful for the first time to discriminate against Travellers. Having witnessed racism and exclusion, Travellers now have an expectancy of change being brought into the arena which must be addressed by the policy-makers. Nevertheless, many Travellers might say: *"For my part, I travel not to go anywhere, but to go - I travel for travel's sake. The greatest affair is to move."* (Robert Louis Stevenson)

Travellers must be accepted for who they are, and afforded their rights in all aspects of health care.

Working in partnership with the community, enabling them to identify some of their needs, and empowering them to start making changes, whilst recognising and taking into account their culture, can be seen to have had many positive outcomes and been very rewarding. I have had a lot of support and advice from Craigavon Travellers' Support Committee and the Community Workers. My own colleagues, especially the Community Health Worker and School Nurse, have given practical help. The network of health visitors and community workers aligned to the Traveller community throughout Northern Ireland has provided much-needed information when families move, and this affords them some continuity of care.

However, there are many unresolved health issues relating directly to the environment Travellers are forced to live in. It is to be hoped that the 'Targeting Social Needs' initiative which has pointed out the needs of the Traveller community as suffering particular types of disadvantage, will address the inequalities of health care, and subsequently lower the morbidity rate and raise their life expectancy to come into line with the settled community.

References

Craigavon Travellers' Support Committee, Annual Reports 1994-1997, Craigavon Travellers Support Committee, Craigavon.

Ginnety, Dr P (Year) A Report on the Health of Travellers, p 34, EH&SSB.

Howes, D (1997) Gypies, Travellers and the Health Service, p 23, The Policy Press, University of Bristol.

Lazenbatt, Dr A (1994) Health and Wellbeing Into the Next Millennium.

Molloy, S (1998) Accommodating Nomadism, Report Travellers' Movement, Northern Ireland.

Department of Health & Social Services (1998) New Targeting Social Need, HMSO, Belfast.

Mann-Kler, D (1997) Out of the Shadows. An Action Research Report into Families, Racism and Exclusion in Northern Ireland, Barnardo's, Belfast.

Twinn, S and Cowley, S (1992) Principles of Health Visiting and Examination, Health Visiting Association and the UK Standard Conference on Health Visitor Education.

Advisory Committee on Travellers for Northern Ireland (1992) With, Not For Conference Report, ACT NI, Belfast.

9   Using a Community Development Approach to Develop Good Practice in Working with Children and Young People

A Partnership Between the Southern Health & Social Services Board and Away From Home and Safe

Ann Godfrey and Patricia Gormley

Introduction

This Chapter describes a project designed to address specific training needs in the community sector within a particular geographical area. The project is a result of a partnership between a statutory agency, the Southern Health & Social Services Board (SHSSB) and a voluntary organisation, 'Away from Home and Safe' (AFH&S). AFH&S is a federation of groups which care for children and young people when they are away from home on holidays or residentials. As the training needs were within the community sector, the approach used was a community development one. The pilot stage of the project has been monitored and evaluated, and this Chapter addresses the perceived benefits of such an approach.

Background

The training needs for the community groups involved in childcare were twofold; firstly for training on the Children (NI) Order 1995 and secondly for training in child protection and good practice in working with children and young people. These two sets of needs were identified separately by the Board and AFH&S.

The SHSSB, recognising that the community sector provides significant amounts of care for children and families, provides training to support this work in a number of ways. However, despite the fact that the Children (NI) Order 1995 was implemented in November 1996, training had not been provided to the community sector on the Children Order. The Children Order training strategy within the SHSSB was guided by and resourced through a regional Children Order training strategy devised by the Department of Health & Social Services Regional Steering Group which contained no provision for the community sector. This seems to be in part due to the lack of a workable model of dissemination of the training. In addition, neither the DHSS, nor the statutory or voluntary childcare sectors had been able to identify or quantify that part of the community sector which would benefit from Children Order training. The need was becoming apparent by community groups approaching the SHSSB and its constituent Health & Social Services Trusts to request training on the Order. Though there was agreement that the training was needed, existing structures were seen as ill-equipped to deliver training which would be accessible to and appropriate for the community sector. Discussions were ongoing when AFH&S approached the SHSSB regarding another training need.

'Away From Home and Safe' promotes good practice and endeavours to ensure the protection and wellbeing of children while they are away from home. This is achieved through the maintenance of a Code of Good Practice, and making available advice, support and training in relation to it.

Early in 1993, as a result of a letter they had received from a young woman who had been sexually abused whilst on a holiday scheme ten years previously, the NSPCC contacted several holiday organisations, to see what level of awareness there was amongst groups concerning the wellbeing and protection of children, and what standards were being applied when taking children and young people away from home. A Committee was formed of interested groups and individuals who organised two major conferences. The outcome was the publication - Away From Home and Safe – 'A Code of Good Practice'. Following this, funding was obtained from the DHSS and the four Health & Social Services Boards to appoint a Development Officer. The Development Officer was appointed in 1995, and since this time has been providing training, advice and support to community and voluntary groups across Northern Ireland on the issues of child protection, running safe residentials and protecting children staying with host families.

In the light of the Children (NI) Order 1995, it was important for AFH&S to link with the Health & Social Services Trusts and the Health & Social Services Boards' Area Child Protection Committees - in order to build working relationships and look strategically at the way forward for child protection across Northern Ireland.

In efforts to meet the demands, AFH&S has had to develop strategically through the development of a number of partnerships with statutory and voluntary bodies.

During 1996, it became apparent that it was an impossible task to provide training for the numerous groups across Northern Ireland providing services for children and young people. There was a need to develop a long-term strategy to ensure that organisations have the expertise to provide ongoing child protection training for all their staff and volunteers. It became important to focus on the development of a cascade training strategy in order to address the long-term needs of the community.

In addition the need for Children Order training had been raised consistently by community groups on previous AFH&S training events. AFH&S had become increasingly concerned about the lack of training on the Children Order, and the very real fears community groups were articulating about their lack of knowledge of what this 'new' legislation would mean for them in practical terms for running their groups. There was also confusion expressed about the difference between the Children Order and 'child protection'.

In order to address this, AFH&S approached the SHSSB to explore the possibilities of working in partnership. The two organisations began work on how to disseminate good practice to community groups working with children and young people, concentrating on the Children Order and child protection.

'Community Sector Training'

The result of these discussions was the formulation of a joint project, the 'Community Sector Training', managed by the SHSSB and AFH&S and funded by the DHSS from October 1997 to July 1998.

Rationale of the Training

The Children Order requires that a range of family support be provided to meet the needs of a specifically-defined group of children in need. The regulations and guidance accompanying the Order clearly state that a community development model should constitute part of the strategy for delivering support to families. To achieve this, the statutory, voluntary and community sectors must develop a common language in which to debate family support, and formulate new provision to meet assessed needs. One of the steps in developing such a common language is arriving at a shared knowledge base. Lack of training on the Children Order for the community sector was likely to hinder a shared approach to family support.

The mechanism for co-ordinating services for children and families will be the formulation of Children Services Plans by each Health & Social Services Board from 1999 onwards. These plans will incorporate, in written form available to the public, details of all family support provision. The required method for arriving at these plans is through co-operation with statutory and voluntary organisations and the community. Prior to this training community groups were demonstrating that, far from being in a position to be involved in such discussion, they were feeling vulnerable and concerned about how the new legislation would affect them. Training which empowers the community sector through knowledge of the Order would play an important part in facilitating groups taking part in discussions on family support.

The community sector also requires the training in child protection and good practice provided by AFH&S. Given the complications of small community groups accessing training, and their identified confusion about the distinction between the Children Order and child protection training, it would seem to make sense to amalgamate all the training. There are practical advantages in this. However, just as important is the ability to deliver messages about child protection and the imperatives in the Children Order that services should be provided to the wider group of 'children in need' within the same programme. Bringing this material together would facilitate understanding of, and contribution to what is known as the 'refocusing debate' on the child protection/family support interface. This refers to the importance of organisations meeting the needs of children in their families, before the crisis point of intervention through the statutory child protection procedures is reached.

This interface has mostly been addressed in discussion within statutory agencies, but some of the difficult issues lie at the community/statutory agency interface, and discussion is needed here also (Jordan, 1997). Though aiding such discussion was not the aim of the training, having an understanding of the basics could only aid any such discussion in the future.

The Process

In order to look at the provision of training within the community, AFH&S contacted a number of key people involved in the local community. These included Community Workers employed by two local community development organisations and the Team Leader of a Community Work Team within a local Health & Social Services Trust. Meetings were held between AFH&S, SHSSB and the above Community Workers. It was agreed that it would be important to adopt a community development approach to addressing training needs. By this is meant an approach which: *"includes participation, empowerment and self-help ... which helps to realise the potential of both individuals and groups within communities"* (Community Development Review Group, 1991). Decision-making would involve the community and training would be delivered through a ''cascade' model, so that local community representatives would receive training and cascade it to groups. It was felt that this model would leave much more expertise within the community itself than, for instance, employing outside 'experts' to deliver the training. Both SHSSB and AFH&S had experience of using this model. It had allowed trainers to take ownership of the material, and to 'stand alongside' those they are training, as they are involved in similar activities themselves.

It was also felt that training for the community sector would work only if it was planned and co-ordinated so that it was accessible to small and disparate groups. It would need to take into account their differing needs, including those such as the safety of particular areas and venues for particular groups. Such planning would require a Project Worker, whose role would be to liaise with the community sector throughout the SHSSB area and to organise the practical arrangements for the training. Critically, the way in which the project was planned and progressed would have to follow community development principles, particularly in terms of taking direction from community representatives about how the project should be run.

In order to share the proposal with the wider community, a seminar was organised, and community groups from across the SHSSB area were invited. Forty-five community representatives attended, from a wide range of groups. These included small locality-based groups which were running or starting up varied activities, including mother and toddler groups and after school groups. Also included were sports groups, church groups, youth groups, Travellers' support groups, and some larger organisations like Women's Aid, who sent local representatives. There was overwhelming agreement that Children Order and child protection training was needed, and that the proposal was a good way of bringing this training to the community.

At the seminar, participants were invited to become part of a Community Reference Group, which would ensure the influence of the community on the project. A Project Officer was appointed, and at the first meeting of the Community Reference Group it was decided to break this down into three local Community Reference Groups - one per Trust area (as the area as a whole covers a large population of roughly 270,000) to facilitate travelling and childcare arrangements.

Role of Community Reference Groups

The role of the Community Reference Groups is as follows: to facilitate ownership of the project by the community sector, using existing networks; to provide the Project Officer with information, using existing networks regarding for example which groups require training, venues, groups, and potential trainers; to advise the Management Group on issues raised by the training; and to contribute to the evaluation of the project.

A management group was formed in order to make formal links into each of the three Health & Social Services Trusts. Its role was overall management; decision making regarding, for example groups targeted for training and access to training; a formal link to the Child Protection panels in each Trust to inform about issues raised in training; dissemination of evaluation and outcomes of the project to Trusts, Boards and the community sector.

The Role of Project Officer Was: To organise and attend meetings of Community Reference Groups and Management Groups; to liaise and audit community groups; to co-ordinate selection of trainers; to co-ordinate (production of training), to co-ordinate and participate in the 'training the trainers' programme; to co-ordinate the identification of groups requiring training and training events; and to write an evaluation report.

Training Materials

The Training Pack 'Keeping Safe' developed by Away From Home and Safe and Our Duty to Care Project (Northern Ireland Volunteer Development Agency) was adapted for this project. A module on the Children Order was provided by SHSSB. Modules on child protection and good practice were adapted from 'Keeping Safe', with inclusions on the Children Order where appropriate.

Training the Trainers

Twenty-eight people from community groups within the SHSSB area volunteered to undergo training as trainers. There was extensive discussion within the Community Reference Groups and the Management Group on the selection of trainers. The issue was how to be inclusive in terms of reaching people at grass roots level, and at the same time to make sure that anyone providing child protection training would be able to manage appropriately the difficult situations which frequently arise. Criteria such as previous experience of providing child protection training were avoided, which would have excluded the vast majority of people working in community groups. Instead, there was assessment on an ongoing basis throughout the 'training the trainers' process. This was a two-way process: each community trainer was continually assessing whether they felt able to provide such training, and the AFH&S and SHSSB trainers, ourselves, were assessing the ability of the trainers to manage the material. This process has continued into monitoring the training itself.

The trainers come from a variety of backgrounds and experiences which range from youth and community work, training, counselling, voluntary work in the community, adult literacy, parenting, sports groups, church groups and early years groups. The variety and wealth of knowledge and experience brought to this project by the trainers is reflected in the enthusiasm for the training and in the extremely positive evaluations.

Evaluation of the 'Training the Trainers' Programme

The evaluations in relation to the training the trainers process were very positive:-

- 28 participants began and completed the programme.
- 50% had heard about the training through information circulated, while 46% had heard about the training by word of mouth.
- 96% of participants felt that the planning and organisation of the training was excellent.
- 100% of participants felt all the objectives for the training were met, highlighting the success of the programme.
- 89% felt that the training was very relevant to their work, while the remaining 11% felt it was 'relevant'.

In terms of how the training would help the participants to deliver the training to groups the following comments were made:

- Give confidence   89%
- Develop presentation skills   93%
- Increase knowledge and awareness   93%
- More comfortable with material   93%
- Knowing that there will be support   89%

- 100% of participants felt that the trainers had the ability to put the subject across.
- 89% felt that the training took into account the need to provide a service equally to all children and families, bearing in mind religion, racial origin, disability etc.

- 89% of participants assessed the course as "excellent", with one participant assessing it as "good" and one, "above average".

Support to the Community Trainers

The issue of support has been seen as crucial to the experience of the trainers in terms of increasing confidence by discussing issues which arise, and ensuring the quality of the training. The Community Trainers, AFH&S and SHSSB Trainers and Project Officer decided upon the form of support together. A series of recall days were held, with Community Trainers sharing experiences and learning from each other. In addition, individual support was available by telephone, mainly from the Project Officer.

The Training

The training itself has now been delivered. In the period from April 1998 to July 1998, 111 training sessions were delivered to a range of community groups in the SHSSB area. The groups which have accessed the training are largely those small groups which are not affiliated to larger bodies, and who cannot access training from any other source. They were frequently groups, usually called 'development groups' or 'community associations', which carry out a number of different activities with children and young people as need arises in their communities. Other categories of groups which have accessed the training are as follows: sports groups, youth groups, mother and toddler groups, crèches, church groups, Irish language groups, larger community development associations, activity centres, women's groups and local representatives of larger organisations like Women's Aid.

Outcomes

The training has been evaluated and monitored throughout, to establish the outcomes.

The method of evaluation was to require each participant on each training module to complete a comprehensive evaluation form at the end of the training event, and to analyse a sample of the results using SPSS software. The evaluation sample analysed was made up as follows:

Trainers: Sessions provided by 21 out of the 24 Trainers who delivered training were included. This represents an 84% sample of Trainers. (Note: the three Trainers whose evaluations were not included in the sample to be analysed were chosen for monitoring.)

Modules: The training consists of five modules. Examples of all five modules were included.

Sessions: The sample consisted of 50 sessions of the 111 sessions delivered. This represents a 45% sample of sessions.

Findings

In terms of finding out about the training, a letter to their group notified 41% of the participants, and 36% found out by word of mouth. This demonstrates the importance of local networks in disseminating information about the training.

NOTE: In all figures the values of questions not answered at all are not given, but can be seen to be small in all cases.

When asked about the quality of venues 87 % said they were "good or excellent", whereas only 2% said that they were "below average".

In terms of the planning and organisation of the training 36% of the participants reported it as "good", 57% as "excellent", and only 3% as "unsatisfactory". This was an important finding, given the high priority attached to making the training accessible to community groups.

Participants were asked whether the objectives of training were "met", "partially met" or "not met". Each module had a number of objectives. The figure given in the table below is an average across the objectives for each module.

Module	Objectives Met (%)	Objectives Partially Met (%)	Objectives Not Met (%)
1	90	0	1
2	89	2	0
3	97	1	0
4	95	0	2
5	90	0	2

As can be seen from the table, overwhelming numbers of the participants on each of the modules thought that the objectives had been met.

In terms of the training being relevant to their work, 67% said it was "very relevant", 24% "relevant", 7% "some relevance" and only 1% felt that it had "no relevance".

The participants were asked if the Trainers had the ability to put the subject across: 99% answered "yes", and only 1% answered "no" to this question. This was an important finding, given the cascade model of training.

A similarly large percentage, 94% thought that the training had addressed the need to provide services equally, across differences such as racial origin and religion, while only 3% thought that this had not been addressed. The participants were asked if they found it useful having training on the Children Order and child protection in the same programme: 96% said they found it useful, and only 1% thought that it was not.

Their overall assessment of the training was that 62% rated the training as "excellent", 33% as "good" and 3 % as "above average".

The participants also described a wealth of ways in which they thought they would put the training into action. Some examples are:

- 76% of participants on the Children Order module thought that they would now be able to refer children in need for support, while 58% were going to talk to their group about the concept of family support and what it might mean for them.
- 62% of participants on the Awareness of Abuse module said that they would share what they had learned about the nature of abuse with others in their group and 83% said that they would now be better able to pick up signs of abuse.
- 85% of participants on the Policies and Procedures module thought that they would be better able to develop reporting procedures in their group.
- 88% of those who attended the Code of Behaviour module felt that they had an understanding of how to develop self–protection when working with children and young people and 77% thought that their group would be able to begin to develop a Code of Behaviour
- 86% of those who attended the module on residentials felt that they would be better able to develop policies and procedures for residentials, while 76% said they would discuss the issues raised in their groups.

Overall, as can be seen, the evaluation was overwhelmingly positive. One note of caution in terms of these findings is that those receiving this training had received very little similar training, and were very enthusiastic. In addition, the fact that the Community Trainers did come from similar situations as the participants increased a positive atmosphere on the training, which may have prevented some negative comments being recorded. However, even bearing the possibility that such factors could have affected the results, they do demonstrate a very high satisfaction rating for the training.

Monitoring

Monitoring has been carried out on a sample of just under half of the Trainers providing training. This, too, has demonstrated consistently good quality in terms of the delivery. It has also given the SHSSB and AHF&S monitors and the Project Officer the opportunity to observe the dynamics of the group process. The benefit of the training being delivered by community representatives has been that the participants clearly feel at ease, and they will raise issues which they would be unlikely to raise with a 'professional', especially a Social

Worker. The sessions have an atmosphere of self-development, and are clearly seen by the participants as part of developing their work with children and young people. Comments like *"our group are going to sit down at the end of the five sessions and see how we can bring the training into our work"* are common. The monitoring showed that providing the training in this way changed its meaning from a fairly traditional imparting of information on good practice, to an opportunity for groups to take and use the input in a much more active and creative way than is often the case when training is offered to people working within the statutory sector. It seemed that the training could be used to *"...support community groups in resolving concerns as group members define them..."* (Labonte, 1996), which activity Labonte calls 'community development'.

Outcomes for the Community Trainers

The Community Trainers were, for the most part, people who had never provided any kind of training before and certainly not child protection. During the 'training the trainers' process there was a noticeable change in their confidence, not only with the particular material, but also in terms of presentations in general. For instance, one person who had been working in the community sector for many years and who was very comfortable with working with groups, had felt unable to ever give a formal presentation. She now feels that she can not only provide the present training, but also feels confident to do presentations in her own work. Another of the Trainers, at the end of the 'training the trainers' process, said that the training has made her realise that she had been at home with her children for too long, and she needed to 'get out there'. She has now provided a series of training sessions that have all been evaluated as "excellent".

The Trainers were typical of members of community groups in that, previously, their knowledge base was weak in the area of child protection, and most came from groups which had only just begun to develop policies on child protection or good practice. This was to be expected, given the lack of infrastructure and support to such groups. The change in the Trainers was dramatic, in terms of their knowledge and confidence. One Trainer recently addressed a large Gaelic Athletic Association meeting on the merits of child protection training, and talked of his owns real doubts and reluctance to face the uncomfortable issues raised, but stressed the importance of doing so.

The Community Trainers, as a group, have taken ownership of the training, and have taken on promoting the training in their communities. This, together with the 'word of mouth' dissemination of information about the training from participants is proving very effective for small groups to learn about and choose to access the training. This process is likely to enable the wider community to take ownership of the issues raised within the training, which is likely to lead to creating a safer environment for children and young people in this community.

Outcomes for the Partner Organisations and the Community

Through the partnership, a process has developed whereby the community sector has been able to access training in a way which is developmental. The training has reached small, non-affiliated groups, through natural local networks, and has also begun to establish new links between the statutory and community sector. The view of AFH&S is that this was possible only because of the willingness of the Board to look at the issues and consider a way forward when approached by AFH&S. From the viewpoint of SHSSB, through using the expertise of AFH&S in working with the community and disseminating good practice work with children and young people, the partnership enabled it to work with the community sector in a way which is unusual for a statutory body. The Children Order has initiated a debate about how best to work in partnership with parents in terms of organising or making accessible services to children in need. There are many blocks to this, given the responsibilities of statutory agencies for child protection (Jordan, 1991), so it would seem that any project such as this, which has the potential to break down traditional barriers, could help the overall task of working in partnership, the Board and AFH&S are of the opinion that the Project Worked because differing expertise was respected, there was flexibility, the workload was shared equally and, above all, there was good communication - especially between the partners and the Project Officer. It also seems important to the success of the project so far, that both partners had experience of cascade training, and were aware of the support and guidance needed to make sure that the end product for groups is of sufficiently high quality.

In terms of the relationship between the statutory sector and the community sector the project was unusual. The partnership itself, between a statutory body and a voluntary body, involved, from the outset, differing 'world views' and areas of expertise, as stated above. The relationship with the community sector was facilitated by the Community Reference

Groups, and by the Trainers themselves. The viability of the Community Reference Groups varied, in that in two Health & Social Services Trust areas they were sustained by the same group of people throughout, and gave invaluable direction to the project. The Community Reference Group in the third area was much less successful, with varying membership and made little real impact on the overall direction of the project. The take-up of training in this area was also lower. A major factor which may have led to this difference, was that in this area there was no Community Development Worker employed by the Health & Social Services Trust. In the other two areas, the input from these workers was crucial, as the link that they provided eased communication between community groups and ourselves.

The Future

The demand for the training has grown since the end of the pilot project. It appears that messages about the training being worthwhile and useful have started to flow within the natural networks of the community.

Due to this increased demand, and advice from the Community Reference Groups that the training would be needed on an ongoing basis, an application for future funding was made to the DHSS. This application reflected the fact that, by the nature of community involvement, much of it in a voluntary capacity, some of those people who have received training this year will be replaced by others next year, who would also need the training. In addition, in time, the content of the training will need to be extended, as groups identify new needs arising from their work.

The application for funding was for a project to carry on the tried and tested partnership between AHF&S and the SHSSB. It will continue to build on existing resources, ie the Community Trainers, and the networking carried out within the community sector in the SHSSB area.

Some lessons from the experience of the present project have been incorporated. For example, it includes a full-time Project Worker, with administrative support, based in a community setting within the SHSSB geographical area. The pilot project involved three offices, two Administrative Officers and three bases (different from the three offices!) for distribution of materials and equipment. The fact that this caused very little confusion was very much to do with the level of communication achieved. However, the experience points to the importance of having one, known, local base.

Funding has now been secured for a two-year project from the DHSS and the SHSSB, and a Project Worker and Office Administrator have been appointed. The project is housed in an office within a community centre locally, and is currently identifying new groups requiring training.

The community development model will continue to be used in the new project. The importance of setting enough time aside for building up relationships and networking with community groups cannot be underestimated. Community Reference Groups, which have been a critical mechanism to ensure the community-driven direction of the project, will continue. In addition, links into the Health & Social Services Trusts will be maintained, so that issues arising from the training can be fed back into the Trusts.

Conclusion

Community development: *"...encourages individuals and groups to bring their knowledge, skills and energies to bear in extending the range of facilities available within their own areas, and in negotiating future development with the relevant statutory and voluntary agencies..."* (Community Review Group, 1991). Also, *"...by enabling people to share their skills and knowledge, community development promotes learning through informal and social education "* (Gilchrist, 1995).

Labonte, when considering the components of community development states that: *"Community development describes an empowering relationship between state institutions and community groups."* (Labonte, 1996).

We would argue that the Community Sector Training project, both in terms of the experiences of the Community Trainers and the participants, is acting in this empowering way. Partnership, as required under the Children Order, and 'working together', as indicated in the body of research on child protection, would seem to be enhanced by this process. If that is the case, this form of dissemination of good practice can only add to the efforts of all those currently working towards better care and safety of children.

References

Community Development Review Group (1991) <u>Community Development in Northern Ireland: A Perspective for the Nineties</u>, Community Review Group, Belfast.

HMSO, (1996) <u>Children's Order (NI) 1995</u>, HMSO, Belfast.

Gilchrist, A (1995) <u>Community Development and Networking</u>, Standing Conference for Community Development and Community Development Foundation.

Jordan, B (1997) 'Partnership With Service Users in Child Protection and Family Support', in N Parton, (ed) <u>Child Protection and Family Support</u>, Routledge, London.

Labonte, R (1996) <u>The Language of Community Development: Future Directions</u>. Paper delivered October 4-6, 1996. Kingston, Ontario.

10 Empowerment with a Safety Net – Supported Volunteer Placements

Brian Drury

Craigavon & Banbridge Volunteer Bureau (CBVB) is a small, but effective, independent charity whose aims are to develop and support volunteering opportunities for people in its local area. It is one of ten Volunteer Bureaux in Northern Ireland who together provide support for much of the volunteer work that takes place in the Province. CBVB is well placed to make an effective contribution to the work of community development in Craigavon. It has developed strong partnerships with many voluntary groups in the area, and works closely with key departments within health and social services in developing community initiatives.

In January 1997, it began a two-year pilot project aimed at developing volunteering opportunities for people with physical disabilities and/or mental ill-health. This was the first project of its kind to carried out by a Volunteer Bureau in Northern Ireland and it was hoped that the lessons learned would have an effect in the wider volunteer network throughout the Province.

Why Do People Volunteer?

The perception of volunteering is something that has changed over the years. It is widely accepted that a volunteer is an individual who undertakes work for the benefit of others, outside of their immediate family, undertaken by free choice and not directly in return for wages. However, it is also now recognised that few people who undertake this kind of work are driven purely by altruistic motives.

Many people simply like to 'do their bit' for a cause close to their heart, or as their contribution to the local community. For others, and this is certainly true of the majority of people who walk through the door of CBVB, the words 'volunteering' and 'employment' are inextricably linked. Volunteering offers a wide range of opportunities for those involved: it can provide that vital first notch on the CV, indeed it can provide practical experience and training required for many disciplines from shopwork to broadcasting. It can offer the flexibility to try things out for those who feel paid employment to be a daunting possibility, and perhaps most importantly it can offer a practical and long-term alternative to those whose employment opportunities are restricted by other factors such as disability and benefit legislation.

> *"I volunteer for a group that helps the families of people who are mentally ill. I work in the office typing out letters and helping out by doing things like answering the phone.*
>
> *"I have a visual impairment so I thought it would be hard to get a placement, but the extra support scheme installed a package which means I can use the computer in the office I work in. They also provided me with a magnifier which I use to read documents that need to be word processed.*
>
> *"I really enjoy my work, and hope that the experience I am gaining will help me find a job working in an office."*
>
> *Male Volunteer (22)*

Background to the Project

It is from the background of this understanding that CBVB developed its current Extra Support Needs Project. The training needs of the volunteer have long since been a recognised priority aim of the Bureau. This is reflected in the funding structure of the organisation, a large part of which is provided by the Government's Training and Employment Agency, who support the Volunteer Training Programme through which the vast majority of CBVB's volunteers are placed.

This programme targets young and unemployed people in the local area and offers practical training in two key ways. Firstly, a volunteering placement will be developed with an agency within the statutory or voluntary sectors. The Bureau works with a range of agencies in the Craigavon and Banbridge areas and can offer a wide variety of opportunities to potential volunteers. Clearly, the needs of the target groups vary, and placement agencies are carefully selected to ensure that adequate support and supervision exists, and the particular needs of the volunteer are understood and addressed.

The second aspect is that of practical training, which is either sourced through colleges of further education and other training organisations or provided directly by the Volunteer Bureau. The Bureau offers basic training in a number of areas including confidence-building and personal development, assertiveness, basic literacy, numeracy and communication skills. Computer Literacy and Information Technology (CLAIT) training is also provided on site in the Bureau's computer suite. Each volunteer also undertakes a training needs analysis, and a training budget for each volunteer is available to fund appropriate accredited courses at the Upper Bann Institute of Further Education.

In 1996, the Bureau secured funding made available through the European Union Peace and Reconciliation Programme to employ a Placement and Access Officer. Essentially 'peace dividend money', this Programme was aimed at supporting community projects in Northern Ireland and the surrounding border counties involved in developing social inclusion and cross-community initiatives. The provision of equal opportunities to people, regardless of their perceived religion, is very much an integral part of Bureau policy. A good example would be in the support it has shown to volunteers from both sides of the sectarian divide who live on the Garvaghy Road in Portadown.

Project Aims

The Extra Support Needs Programme began in earnest in January of 1997 when the Placement and Access Officer came into post. The main identified aims were: to recruit volunteers with disabilities; to develop support mechanisms which are client-specific; to identify, and as best possible remove, physical and attitudinal barriers to volunteering, to develop partnerships with statutory and voluntary organisations which promote and support disabled volunteering; to develop and promote good practice in relation to equal opportunities for disabled people who wish to volunteer.

Over fifty people benefited from the scheme in the first eighteen months, undertaking volunteering placements in a variety of different placements involving shopwork, advice work, be-friending schemes, environmental projects, women's groups, journalism, computer work and volunteer driving schemes. Many of the people involved now consider volunteering to be their job: for others it is a step in the right direction towards their goal of paid employment. Some come to the Scheme with a wealth of employment experience and are looking for the opportunity to redevelop their confidence after a period of mental ill-health; others come from day centres and may be accessing the opportunity to work for the first time in their lives.

Why Involve Volunteers With Extra Support Needs?

In order to promote the inclusion of volunteers with disabilities to potential placement organisations and to other volunteer organisers, the Bureau had to identify practical reasons why organisations should consider involving volunteers with extra support needs.

Firstly, it would be seen as good practice, particularly as many of the organisations approached were involved in disability issues themselves. There was also an obligation under certain legislation, particularly the Disability Discrimination Act of 1995 and the Care in the Community Act of 1993.

Many organisations have major difficulties recruiting and keeping volunteers. The issue of supply and demand could, therefore, be used as a good argument for those considering developing volunteer placements for people with disabilities. Whilst there is an ever-increasing competition between organisations to recruit volunteers, demographic changes have resulted in fewer people to fill these placements.

The third reason was simply that people with disability had much to gain from volunteering. For some it can offer the opportunity to gain training, work experience and that all-important first reference. It can provide the flexibility to try out different types of work and gain new skills without their benefits being affected. The benefit trap is a major issue affecting many people with disabilities: volunteering can provide the 'experience of work' for those who feel they are unable to enter paid employment.

Volunteering can provide a stake in the community for those who feel socially excluded or isolated. For someone recovering from a mental illness, for example, it can provide a structure to their week, social contact, a sense of empowerment and the opportunity to build their confidence and self-esteem in a supported environment.

Finally, and most importantly, volunteers with disabilities have much to offer. It is not simply good practice to involve people with disabilities, it would seem wise to harness the wealth of skill and experience that they have to offer. Many of the apparent disadvantages of disablement can be turned to advantages for voluntary activity.

Once established in their work, a volunteer with special needs can offer a high level of time and commitment. Time itself can be a burden for those who have nothing to fill it, yet is a scarce commodity in many organisations. Such volunteers may be able to offer experience in specialist areas, such as drug abuse or disability benefits, and offer sensitivity and understanding stemming from personal experience.

Recruitment

Volunteers are recruited in many different ways: poster campaigns, local media, special events and particularly, in the experience in Craigavon, word of mouth; so it was first of all important to ensure that any promotional literature or message made it clear that people with disabilities were welcome and what level of support would be available to them.

> *"R kept telling everyone at the day centre how much he enjoyed his volunteering so I thought I might try it myself. After reading one of the leaflets I gave them a 'phone and next thing I knew I was a volunteer myself."*
>
> *Male Volunteer (39)*

The most successful way of specifically targeting potential volunteers for the scheme was, however, seen to be the referral system set up with organisations involved in providing services to people with disabilities. These included local day centres, social workers, GPs, occupational therapists, and charities involved in disability issues. As well as being an effective way of recruiting volunteers, the referral system also proved to be an important source of support and information from key individuals who had detailed knowledge or personal experience of volunteers needs, and were often able to offer advice and practical support.

Voluntary work is not always the appropriate step for a person to take at that particular time, therefore it was important to draw up guidelines for potential referral organisations to consider. A day centre threatened by closure, for example, might attempt to refer someone to do voluntary work, because they feel there are no other options available to them. This could result in an unsuccessful placement, which can be upsetting for the volunteer and cause difficulties for the placement organisation.

Developing Support Mechanisms

The level and type of support required was found to vary quite dramatically from volunteer to volunteer. Someone who is established in their role and is well supported by the organisation that they are placed in, is unlikely to require the same number of visits from an Access Officer as a volunteer who has just started working in a newly-developed placement with a supervisor who is unfamiliar with working with volunteers.

When considering the level of extra support that could be provided, it was found that it was best to assess the needs of each volunteer individually, and then draw up a development plan which took into account their needs, the resources available by the placement organisation and any available input from external factors such as key workers or community transport schemes.

By taking time at the start to match each volunteer with an appropriate placement the aim was to attempt to keep the amount of long term extra support required to a minimum. The emphasis is always placed on the person's ability, rather than their disability; therefore if the appropriate groundwork is carried out at the start, then it should be possible, once a routine has been settled, for each volunteer to get in and get on with the job that they have been placed to do.

Examples of the type of pre-placement preparation being discussed here would include: installing specialist computer packages to enable a person with visual impairments to fulfil a placement involving computer administration work; making minor adjustments to the layout of a building to make it more accessible for a person using a wheelchair; or matching an able-bodied volunteer who will work along-side a person with limited mobility and provide them with assistance when requested.

This method is obviously not an exact science - not every placement has been a success - but the application of a flexible approach by everyone involved to allow for unforeseen difficulties or changes, has meant that the majority of volunteers have enjoyed successful and rewarding placements.

Although CBVB's Extra Support Scheme is the first of its kind in Northern Ireland, a number of similar projects exist within volunteer bureaux in other parts of the UK. Each project is unique in the way it operates, and the client group with which it works. Together with workers from these projects, CBVB was involved in agreeing a number of models which can help to describe the different type of work that can be involved in supporting volunteers with extra support needs. Although CBVB's Project probably best fits into the inter-agency model, our approach to helping volunteers can be reflected in aspects of all of the following five models.

Models of Volunteer Support

Client-Specific: This provides a focus on a particular group, for example young adults with a learning disability, or people with sensory impairments.

Universal: This model covers all types of special need. The support provided depends very much on the needs of the individual. One disabled volunteer might simply require assistance finding an accessible venue in which to do their work; another might require extensive training and support over a long period of time.

Independence Model: This will only work if it is believed that volunteers could work independently once the initial placement work has been completed. Equipment may need to be purchased or a bus route taught, but once this work is done, the volunteer will be self-sufficient in their role.

Partnership Model: Two volunteers work together and support each other, often this will involve a disabled volunteer and an 'able-bodied' volunteer. Both volunteers can be new to the work, or an existing volunteer might be willing to be a partner for either a shorter or longer term.

Inter-Agency Model: Where a number of different organisations are involved in the placement and support of a volunteer. For example a chain of charity shops might provide a number of sheltered placements, a community transport scheme could take them to and from the placement, the Volunteer Bureau would provide ongoing monitoring and support, and Social Services might provide the volunteers through referral.

Physical and Attitudinal Barriers to Volunteering

The Extra Support Scheme has recruited volunteers from a wide variety of backgrounds, each with their own specific needs and abilities. The question of addressing barriers to volunteer opportunities was therefore a complex and ongoing process. It only takes a couple of minutes to identify whether a building will be suitable for a wheelchair user, but there are many other potential obstacles, quite often hidden.

With the exception of advising an organisation on potential sources of funding for structural changes, often very little can be done if the barrier is an obvious physical one, such as a third floor office with no lift facilities. However, once identified most barriers can be removed with surprising ease. Three of the main barriers identified by CBVB, namely benefits, transport and attitudes towards disability, have, it is felt, been tackled with a considerable amount of success.

"I have cerebral palsy and have very limited mobility. I want to do advice work because I am a good communicator but we're having difficulty finding somewhere where the front door works, for me anyway. The Bureau paid for me to go on a counselling course, which I passed, and now I'm hoping to find a door that works soon so that I can put my skills to good use."

Female Volunteer (27)

Social Security Benefits

"I volunteer for Oxfam. I help prepare the stock at their Lurgan Charity Shop. I like working here, I can be a bit shy and it helps me with my confidence to know that I can work in the store or on the shop floor depending.

"I dropped out of volunteering because my husband told me I'd lose my benefits but Brian sent me some information and promised me it wouldn't. I'm really glad I changed my mind."

Female Volunteer (53)

The fear of losing benefits is a very real one for many potential volunteers with disabilities. It was important, therefore, to be familiar at an early stage about the rights of volunteers who are in receipt of benefits. Links were quickly developed with local and head Social Security Offices, as well as advice agencies and welfare rights units.

There are specific rules surrounding disability benefits, and it was useful to clarify these with the DHSS and agree a standard letter for volunteers to advise them on their rights and responsibilities. Volunteers were also offered assistance with any required correspondence. Benefits can be withdrawn on evidence that may seem very slim, and getting them restored can be a long and difficult process. Mistakes can and are made by the DHSS, which could cause potential upset to someone, for example recovering from chronic depression, therefore establishing links with the appropriate people was extremely useful in quickly sorting out a number of potential problems or misunderstandings.

The Rules - 1999

Volunteering does not affect an individual's entitlement to Jobseeker's Allowance, provided they remain available to take up paid employment and actively seek it.

It is likely that a person in receipt of Incapacity Benefit will be restricted to a maximum of fifteen hours' volunteering a week.

Disability Living Allowance is unlikely to be affected by volunteering issues unless this shows that the person's care needs have changed.

Transport

"I heard about the extra support scheme through the local Mental Health Carers' Support Group. One of my sons has quite severe schizophrenia and most of my time is taken up looking after his needs, which can be very demanding at times. I myself am a wheelchair user and I find it difficult to get about, so most of my time is spent in the house. I volunteer at 'Zero-eighteen' writing letters on the computer and answering the 'phone. I need the work to be flexible because of my son, and everyone is very understanding if I can't make it in some days. Volunteering is very important to me, it gets me out of the house and it makes me feel useful.

"For a while I thought I might have to give it up because the fares for the special taxi I use are very expensive for someone on benefits. I explained the situation to my Extra Support Worker, and he arranged for the taxi firm to charge the Volunteer Bureau directly. This is much better and is at least one worry off my mind."

Female Volunteer (43)

Public transport provision is quite poor in Craigavon, particularly in the surrounding rural areas. Public transport for many people with disabilities is virtually non-existent, therefore working out efficient ways of getting volunteers to their placements became a consideration at a very early stage.

Fortunately, the scheme had a travel budget which allowed volunteers unable to access public transport to use taxis. Not all taxis are wheelchair accessible, so relationships were developed with firms that were able to carry wheelchair users. This eventually enabled the Scheme to develop an arrangement whereby the taxi firm invoiced the Volunteer Bureau directly for any volunteer journeys. Most of the volunteers involved were on benefits, which was causing difficulties for them, because they originally were having to wait quite a while for the price of the journey to be reimbursed.

Other avenues that have been explored have included developing links with local community transport schemes, training volunteers to support fellow volunteers who may never have used public transport, and developing volunteer driving schemes.

> *"I am a volunteer driver. I take blind and disabled people swimming on a Monday and Thursday night. I myself have the use of one arm, my wife is a rehabilitation officer for the blind, and it was her that suggested that I get involved.*
>
> *"I can get very short of breath because I have a collapsed lung. Sometimes volunteering can be very frustrating, because there's always some idiot parked in the only disabled space at the swimming pool; but as long as people want to swim I'm happy to do my bit."*
>
> Male Volunteer (62)

Disability Awareness

> *"Everyone here is great, they treat me as an equal. They are very helpful too, but they also wait until I ask.*
>
> *"Me and another disabled volunteer are compiling a guide detailing the accessibility of shops, pubs and leisure facilities in the Craigavon area. It gives details about what's out there for disabled people, and I hope it will encourage more of them to get out and about. I also hope it will make more businesses think about the needs of disabled people."*
>
> Male Volunteer (39)

Practically every organisation approached regarding the placement of a disabled volunteer has responded positively. Many have, quite reasonably, expressed concerns regarding the appropriateness of the placement, or the ability of their organisation to provide sufficient support.

Support for placement agencies has been a vital characteristic of the Scheme, with most doubts being able to be removed at an early stage. This has included developing a substantial library of literature on disability issues, such as fact sheets on specific types of mental illness and handouts on appropriate disability etiquette, which can then be shared with placement agencies when appropriate.

The Bureau has also provided training on issues surrounding disability and volunteering, as well as identified specialised courses that may be of use to particular placement agencies. Encouraging project supervisors not to be afraid to ask their volunteers about how their disability affects them, has allowed for support to be provided more effectively and enabled them to focus on the ability of that person rather than the disability.

The Extra Support Scheme ensures that a disability audit is carried out in each organisation before a placement begins. It is hoped that it will eventually be possible to train up disabled volunteers to carry these out, which would provide valuable focus on an organisation's shortcomings, particularly when considering their responsibility regarding the Disability Discrimination Act.

Conclusion

This chapter focuses on a key aspect of community development in relation to health and social services; the empowerment of socially-excluded individuals and the formation of partnerships between voluntary, statutory and community organisations. Partnerships have led to volunteer referrals, placements, training, support, funding, transport, equipment and expert advice, to name but a few!

A major seminar for volunteer organisers in Northern Ireland was held in Craigavon in November 1998. This also marked the launch of a publication detailing good practice in the support of volunteers with special needs, which is being distributed with the help of the Northern Ireland Volunteer Development Agency and the National Association of Volunteer Bureaux in Great Britain. This is the clearest example of how this Project has striven to meet the fifth aim of developing good practice for disabled volunteers through the dissemination of information to other organisations. However, it is hoped that this dissemination of practice examples is something that has been ongoing throughout the history of the Project, and has had a positive influence on all of the organisations which have been involved in many different ways since the Project began in 1997.

In September of 1998, the Bureau secured additional funding for the Project, enabling it, not only to continue its work, but also to extend the remit to include people with learning disabilities. Although the long-term future is still far from secure, it is hoped that additional funding will eventually be obtained which will allow the Project to work towards the development of specific sheltered projects, which will provide volunteer opportunities for people with particularly severe disabilities.

11 Partnership in Action

Noel McElroy and Stephen Lavery

This Chapter is an example of a working model of partnership between statutory and voluntary service providers and service uses and carers who have a common goal, empowering service users to have a real say in how the services are being provided in their area. It details an emerging Mental Health Forum from its inception, where it is today and future developments exhibiting a community development approach in action.

There were already good working relationships between the statutory and voluntary sector when a new group, The Community Liaison Committee (CLC), was formed to take this forward. The group was concerned with mental health in the Craigavon and Banbridge Community Health & Social Services Trust area. The group's work was assisted by the People First (DHSS, 1990) NI Community Care policy document, which promoted the need for statutory and voluntary organisations to work together, and the ongoing encouragement from Craigavon and Banbridge Community Health & Social Services Trust, our local Trust. This support was on an informal basis, and it was felt that we would need to formalise our meetings and instigate a recognised group or committee, thus in April 1996 the CLC came into being.

Initially the group was made up of three organisations: The Out & About Project (statutory provider), National Schizophrenia Fellowship (NSF) and PRAXIS (voluntary sector provider) and two service users. The inaugural meeting was to lay ground rules and to reach a consensus of opinion as to how the group would function, and to discuss our aims and objectives and common goals. At this meeting, we decided to call ourselves the Community Liaison Committee (CLC).

The group's aims at that time were: to promote existing partnerships between service providers and to encourage involvement of other relevant bodies; to encourage the involvement of service users in the planning and delivery of mental health services in the area; to advocate on behalf of and respond to the needs of service users; to promote awareness of mental health issues in the general public, and promote a 'positive' image of mental health; and to publish a mental health newsletter keeping readers informed of changes taking place in the mental health field.

A catalyst at this time which speeded up the launch of the CLC was the problem service users were encountering in relation to obtaining Disability Living Allowance (DLA). Here we recognised that each of us as service providers were spending considerable time writing letters of support for, or advocating on behalf of service users to the DLA offices regarding claims. We thought that if we combined our efforts they would 'carry more weight' and positively influence decisions made on applications made by people with mental ill health.

We felt as a group that to function effectively and efficiently we would address one major issue at a time in order to reach a solution. So, our first task was to approach the Social Security Head Office dealing with DLA at Belfast, to request a meeting with a view to achieving an understanding of our respective positions, and the difficulties we were experiencing in trying to bridge the 'red tape'. In the interim, we as a group discussed this with the service users in the Craigavon and Banbridge locality, and encouraged them to vent their experiences, worries and aspirations, and to nominate/volunteer someone to become involved in the CLC and attend the meeting with the DLA representatives. The Manager of DLA agreed to meet us along with senior adjudicating officers and a representative from the medical advice service.

This meeting was the first of its type that the DLA branch had experienced, where a consortium of groups and individuals with a common goal asked to meet with them and put forward their views, especially with service users being given the opportunity to explain how the decisions staff make through reviewing application forms, affects individuals' lives.

This was a successful meeting in that it gave both parties the opportunity of putting forward their views, and in partnership working out solutions to these problems. It not only gave the group an insight into how a government body operates, the legislation and boundaries in which they have to work, but it gave DLA staff the opportunity to see how their decisions were impinging on the lives of the applicants for DLA. It 'humanised' the process, and some of the adjudicating officers expressed how in future their working practice would change. It was also an opportunity for us as a group to clarify certain aspects of the legislation, such as therapeutic earnings and voluntary work, which were restricting the opportunities for service users in receipt of DLA. In conclusion, this was a very productive meeting which enabled us to have a 'link person' within the DLA branch who would deal with queries from the Craigavon and Banbridge area.

The success of this meeting strengthened our determination for the CLC to continue and expand. We disseminated the information received from this meeting to other service providers in the Craigavon and Banbridge locality and informed the service users as to its outcome. This led to new members coming on board, both service users and providers, who realised that there is strength in numbers and when those numbers, have a common goal and ethos no problem is insurmountable. This meeting with the DLA has benefited hundreds of applicants within the Craigavon and Banbridge locality, enabling them to overcome the 'red tape' previously associated with DHSS benefits.

Our next major issue was housing within the Craigavon and Banbridge locality, specifically within the Northern Ireland Housing Executive (NIHE) realm. We used the same principles in dealing with this issue as with the last problem. The major concern as expressed by service users was that when they were allocated housing, the NIHE did not take into consideration their mental ill health and in fact the decisions the NIHE were taking were having an adverse effect on their mental and physical wellbeing.

We arranged a meeting with the local managers of the NIHE and put forward our fears and aspirations concerning the services they provide. It enabled them to explain the legislation and procedures to which they must adhere. Once again, a crossover of communication took place, giving each of us an insight as to how the other group worked. We agreed solutions and once again arranged to have a 'link' person within the NIHE to deal with specific issues.

Group Dynamics

This is a good time to reflect on our group and to highlight strengths and weaknesses, to investigate how the group works, why it works and how to improve on its function. A group can be defined as two or more individuals in interaction with each other. All groups share certain characteristics:

Interaction: The members of groups interact with each other. This might mean that they are in direct face to face communication, or that they merely take each other into account.

Shared Goals: The interaction between members of a group does not occur at random - it is organised for a particular purpose, and the achievement of that purpose is usually perceived as desirable by all the members of the group. The nature of the goal will affect the nature and form of the interaction.

Shared Ideology: The members of a group share an ideology which sets the rules for the ways in which they interact with each other and with outsiders. This ideology develops as they interact, and in time the rules will help to define the group and set it apart from other groups.

Established Roles: If group members interact over a lengthy period, the roles they each adopt tend to become better established, allowing communication to flow along expected paths in a predictable manner.

Reflecting on these four characteristics, our group confirms with these criteria. We have shared goals and ideology where we interact with each other face to face, and have established roles. The effectiveness of a group is increased if all its members participate in the group's activities. This is because members who feel that they are making a positive contribution will gain satisfaction from this, and will consequently work to make the group a success. Also, participation by all ensures that the group benefits from the particular skills and expertise of each individual member, and that these members of the group feel that their contributions are valued.

A specific problem we initially encountered was ensuring that each member felt valued and had a say in the direction of the group. Our group not only includes service providers, but also service users and carers. As there was an ongoing partnership between the statutory and voluntary sector, their coming together in a group formation was not a problem, but for the users and carers this was an alien situation.

For years, service users and carers received a service but had no say in how this service was being provided! Now they were in a situation where their views were being actively sought and taken on board. This has taken time to come to the fore: the carers, specifically a local group - Friends and Carers Engaged (FACE), fitted into this consortium very well, and quickly were able to advocate on behalf of their members. Service users' views were encouraged, and through active meetings with them in NSF drop-in centres and Out & About groups, they expressed a desire to become involved. Their progress has been gradual, initially overcoming their fears that their involvement might be tokenistic. Gradually, they came to realise that they were an important and vital part of the CLC, and their views and aspirations regarding what they need from the service providers were not only taken on board, but were actually being put into practice. This is an ongoing process, as the service users can miss some meetings; it is therefore imperative that when they re-attend, they are firstly brought up to date as to what is happening. We also decided as a group that we needed a means of disseminating the information to service users, providers and the general public. We collectively decided we needed a newsletter in order to carry this out.

'The Jag' Newsletter

As we are made up of a collection of agencies/individuals, we were able to locate a local organisation which specialises in publishing which would not only enable us to produce a newsletter, but educate us in how to produce a publication ourselves. This we felt was very important, as it would also provide service users within the Craigavon and Banbridge locality with experience and skills on how to produce a publication, which may lead to voluntary or full-time job opportunities.

We enlisted the help of Brownlow Community Trust (now called Moylinn House Community Development Support Services Agency (CDSSA)), who were very keen to assist us in any way possible. Their Education Worker arranged a meeting with us to discuss this venture. At this meeting we decided on what type of newsletter this would be, its name, content, layout, who was the target group (we decided service users and the general public), what skills we needed to acquire in order to put this into practice, and the timescales involved. Our initial view after this meeting was one of trepidation: this was a huge task to undertake, as we had collectively decided we wanted a professional-looking document, therefore the pressure was on us to collectively put a lot of time and effort into this project. With hindsight, being involved in the production of the newsletter strengthened us as a group, as we were all inexperienced in this field, and so we started on a 'level playing field', and relied on each other for support. Also, the newsletter enabled service users within the Craigavon and Banbridge locality to have an opportunity to have their fears, dreams and aspirations voiced, and have their articles published.

It took six to eight weeks for us to learn the basics of publishing a document. This also gave us the opportunity to encourage service users, carers and those working in the mental health field, to put forward articles and poetry for publication. We also as a group set up an Editorial Committee with relevant sub-groups feeding into the Committee, and elected an Editor to take responsibility for the first two issues, then for someone else from the group to take over for two issues and so on. We also collectively decided that the newsletter would eventually be owned by service users in the Craigavon and Banbridge locality.

Our ethos was that for every service user who became involved, a professional would drop out, until it is eventually edited and distributed by service users, with professional support. The newsletter group will effectively be a part of the CLC, yet independent in what they produce.

It was decided to call the newsletter 'The Jag'. This title was slightly contentious in that it is known within the Mental Health field as a slang term for a 'depot injection' (a means of administering medication with a needle and syringe), but also it could mean a 'Jag' of information - a local colloquialism. It was felt that if the name became an issue, then it was not 'set in stone'; it was stated in the first issue that if a better title can be found, it will be used (to date, no other title has been put forward).

Our first issue was published in December 1997, with a circulation of 250 copies. Since then we have published three issues (at the time of writing the fourth issue was being printed). Our circulation list has dramatically increased to 2,000, which is indicative of the demand for this type of publication. We presently produce the newsletter ourselves from proofreading and editing, and still use Moylinn House CDSSA for technical input with the use of their resource room. It has provided service users and carers with the opportunity of having their materials published; it has shown the depth of untapped talent available, and given them the confidence to participate not only in writing, but getting involved in the production. On reflection, 'The Jag' would not be the publication it is but for the professional input we received at the beginning. The Moylinn House CDSSA Education Worker drew up a production and training analysis so as to ensure we are going in the right direction. We have enlisted professional creative writing and drawing tutors to enable anyone who wants to contribute to 'The Jag' to be educated and assisted in the task, and thus encouraged to develop the skills involved in these areas.

It has not been without its hitches: ensuring that everyone is available for the production has caused some problems. We all have busy working schedules individually, and as 'The Jag' is an add-on to the services we provide individually, ensuring we free time up to involve ourselves in this venture can cause major problems. To co-ordinate time to this involves the participants being 100% committed to the project. Also, ensuring that each individual feels part of the team and is valued by the team is vital if this project is to develop. Having support by our own agencies through Management allowing us time and resources is vital. This publication is not only reflective of the individual participants, but of the organisations they represent.

The first three issues of 'The Jag' were paid for by the Craigavon and Banbridge Community H&SS Trust; the fourth issue was funded by CLC, and future issues will have to be funded by the CLC highlighting and locating potential funding; this is discussed below.

Roadshow

'The Jag' has been a catalyst in encouraging service users to be more assertive and giving them the motivation and desire to exhibit their talents. The 'Prejudice Reduction Roadshow' came into fruition after service users stated that they not only wanted to write about their lives and dreams, but also wanted to express this publicly. We decided as a group from our inception as the CLC to *"...promote awareness of mental health issues in the general public and to promote a positive image of mental health..."* and the Prejudice Reduction Roadshow was an excellent vehicle for achieving this. So on 10th October 1998, World Mental Health Day, we planned a launch of the Roadshow. The whole days' programme belonged to service users - from acting as compere to singing, acting, poetry and self-disclosure. We also decided to invite representatives aged sixteen to eighteen from local secondary schools and students from local technical colleges to attend; representatives from Southern Education & Library Board (SELB); the Mayor of Craigavon and representatives of other relevant bodies. We had no problem enlisting service users to participate, so we booked Lurgan Town Hall as a venue. We provided lunch and had displays from all participants in the CLC as a means of providing information on mental health issues. The day was a complete success with over 140 in attendance; particularly gratifying was that there were over sixty students in attendance. All participants in the event were aged twenty-five on average. This was as planned: the aim was to show that mental ill health can affect anyone at any age, at any time. We called the day 'Everybody Hurts'. Each person attending was given a resource pack which included a programme, Issue 3 of "The Jag" and an evaluation questionnaire. Everyone in attendance took the time to fill in the questionnaire. and five of the schools expressed a desire for us to bring the Roadshow to their schools.

We compiled an evaluation of the day and sent it to the SELB and local schools, who are giving us back a very positive response. We have reduced the show to two hours, which makes it more user-friendly for schools, and enables them to fit it into their curriculum. The SELB have contacted us and are very keen for us to go to youth clubs, and have sent us application forms for grant aid. The feedback from those who participated on the day has been most gratifying in that they are full of confidence and are keen to get involved in the Roadshow. We initially intend to bring this to local schools, and depending on the success of same, may think of widening out to the rest of Northern Ireland. Reflecting on this venture, the easy part was finding and motivating participants. It was the funding of the day with which we had problems, and once again it was through the generosity of the C&DCIISS Trust that we were enabled us to bring this idea to fruition.

Funding

The Community Liaison Committee, through working with the C&BCHSS Trust Community Work Team, has drawn up a Constitution in order to apply for charitable status. It is vital for us to be an independent organisation in order to be a Mental Health Forum, which can challenge directly and have a say in how the Mental Health Service is provided within the Craigavon and Banbridge locality.

It is in acquiring charitable status that we are presently experiencing difficulty. Charitable status is granted by the Inland Revenue, and in order to receive this status there are very specific criteria which have to be met. We are perceived as a consortium of organisations, and at present our involvement collectively in the Prejudice Roadshow is seen as fitting into their criteria. Our production of 'The Jag' newsletter does not fit their criteria as an educational tool, which means we are now setting up 'The Jag' separately as part of the CLC. As a consortium, we provide for and represent 95% of all organisations and individuals concerned with mental health, in the Craigavon and Banbridge locality. Collectively as an organisation, CLC, we are presently in negotiations with a Charities Advisor at Northern Ireland Council of Voluntary Action (NICVA) who specialise in this type of work. Until we attain charitable status we are bereft of resources. We are unable to apply for major funding from bodies such as the National Lottery funding, local Trusts or Northern Ireland Voluntary Trust (NIVT). We are unable as an organisation to open a bank account in our name without a Constitution. We are presently awaiting a solution to this problem.

We are able to function, as we have in the interim set up a Steering Committee with Honorary Chairperson, Treasurer and Secretary. We find the situation frustrating, as we feel that this is having a detrimental impact on the development of the group, preventing us from expanding and diversifying, and making us presently very reliant on our local authority C&BCHSS Trust. They have shown themselves to be committed to community development not only through us, but also through supporting other work in the mental health field such as the 'Policy to Practice' initiative.

Conclusion

As an organisation, CLC, from its inception eighteen months ago, has virtually achieved all its original objectives. We have not only promoted and strengthened our existing partnerships, but have encouraged the involvement of other organisations to the extent where we represent 95% of the service providers in the Craigavon and Banbridge locality. Service user representation has come to the fore with an active user involvement throughout the different programmes, and it has acted as a catalyst for the newly developing 'Out & About' advocacy group developing under the Policy to Practice initiative. The Prejudice Reduction Roadshow is ready and awaiting confirmation from SELB and local school principals, and will commence 'rolling' in the near future. 'The Jag' 4 is our strongest issue to date. We have increased its size from eight pages to twelve pages in order to cater for all the articles and poetry which have been provided by respondents. We feel in order for 'The Jag' to continue its high level of content, we will commence themed issues such as 'Medication', and 'Service Users' Views of the Services They Receive'. As previously stated, we produce, edit and distribute the publication, and are actively trying to improve on the content. Issue 3 included a readers' survey, asking if they were happy with the content, the locality where it was distributed, and so on, and we are actively encouraging service users to become more involved in order to achieve our goal of having 'The Jag' owned by service users. We have an open door policy to service providers and service users.

As we are now approaching the Millennium, we as a group have to reflect on our practice to date; we have to maintain and expand our core membership base, actively encouraging increased involvement from service users, enabling them to feel empowered and active, important members of the group. This will only be achieved through hard work by all participants, and willingness from the Management of respective agencies to incorporate this model of work into all levels of their organisation's practice. Securing charitable status is imperative to maintain and develop present activities, as is highlighting potential funders for training and resources for future programmes and developments. Actively encouraging service users' and carers' involvement in the partnership with statutory and voluntary service providers, ensures an innovative, responsive and well-used service, which is collectively evaluated. This, we feel is a working model of Community Development in practice

Reference

Department of Health & Social Services (1990) People First – Community Care in Northern Ireland, HMSO, Belfast.

12 Social Firms – "It's Our Business to Care"

Mel Byrne

Introduction

Social firms are an example of promoting a community development approach to social integration for people from disability or mental health programmes of care. It may be said that the time has come for such a concept. The initiative developed first on continental Europe, and has steadily grown in popularity so much so that a number of firms have been established here in Ireland and Britain. Mannila (1996) charted their development when they say:

> *"Social Firms are a part of the third sector economy developed since the late 1970s in the Western countries. The ideological background of the third sector is the alternative ideas on civil participation, grass roots democracy locally-focused economic activity propagated by alternative (eg Green, Left or Socially Engaged Religious) thinking."*

Despite this relatively long history of development , the definition of a 'social firm' is still to some extent ambiguous - the main reason for this being that agencies wishing to initiate social firms have been reluctant to exclude participants from engaging, even if they are not taking up full-time employment opportunities. Mannila (1996) offer the following description of social firms:

> *"There are many ways of defining a social firm. Most generally, it can be defined according to two main objectives: to provide a supported setting in which disadvantaged people can learn the skills required to be productive workers and work productively; and to become and be a self-sustaining business that provides long-term employment for its members."*

By defining social firms in this way, the emphasis is on the employee and not the firm. The ethos is to try and ensure that people can be empowered to maximise their potential rather than be marginalised because of their disadvantages. It is this ethos that has attracted the interest of health care providers in Britain and Ireland, as potentially offering an alternative to day care for those with a disability or who have experienced periods of mental ill health. Studies have shown, especially for clients from mental health programmes, that the work environment is therapeutic. As Grove et al (1997) state:

> *"The evidence is therefore very strong that not only does an absence of work (or other socially meaningful activities) have adverse effects on health, but the provision of work can reduce symptoms and improve long-term course and outcome. Work, therefore, is therapy and ensuring that people with mental health problems have access to an adequate range of work activities is probably one of the most important goals for effective community services."*

Many would argue that in relation to the mental health programme the Industrial Therapy movement has adequately catered for that service over the last few decades, both within hospitals and in specialist community-based units. There is a growing awareness, however, that the traditional approaches do not offer a wide enough spectrum of opportunity for the disadvantaged, as they often replicate the stigma of being cared for by the State. Social firms, because of their characteristic of having to run as a business where the client becomes an employee, reduce the level of stigma. As Grove et al (1997) state:

> *"In recent years, we have seen considerable changes in thinking about what should be provided in terms of occupational rehabilitation. Current thinking has moved rather away from traditional 'sheltered workshops' and towards more 'business-like' social firms and co-operatives. This has been very much driven by the need to make services acceptable to a younger generation of service users who want real work, in realistic work environments, not 'make work' in stigmatised settings, with little of interest apparently going on."*

The development of social firms in Northern Ireland and Britain was delayed by dominance of State-organised health and social services providers, who tended to work in isolation from other sectors. It was only when significant changes to the structure of Health & Social Services were brought in, that developments were able to take place in social firms. This structural change was also coupled with a change in social policy which brought a business approach to health and social care provision and promoted a mixed economy of care. In particular, government wanted to see partnerships created between public, private and voluntary sectors. In the Northern Ireland context this was set out in the 1993 government document 'Strategy for the Support of the Voluntary Sector and for Community Development in Northern Ireland' (DHSS, 1992). This has been added to recently with the announcement of a 'Compact' which is a statement of broad principles which will underpin the way every department and agency of government will work with voluntary organisations.

The change in government thinking about the delivery of health and social services was accompanied by a critical examination of day care services by Northern Ireland Social Services Inspectorate in May 1992. In a document entitled 'Inspection of Day Services for Adults with a Mental Handicap/Learning Difficulty in Northern Ireland', the future direction of day care was indicated when the authors made the following points under the sub-title 'Continuing Education':

- They highlighted the projected growth in demand, including 270 school leavers during the next three years, and that social education centres are not always the best place for them.

- The document also states that the growing aspirations of adults with a learning disability in areas such as education, employment and independence will mean growing challenges for their families and professional staff.

- Greater participation needs to take place by creating new structures to involve local communities, educational bodies, employment agencies and interest groups to a much greater extent in caring programmes.

The 'actions required' from these statements included for Health Boards according to the authors are:

- The development of individual packages which better reflect the abilities and aspirations of adults, with the emphasis being on normalising their experiences of being a member of the community.

A review of the current services and development of new initiatives which reflect the changing needs of those concerned.

Although these points refer specifically to those with a learning difficulty, the philosophy was similar across other programmes, such as disability and mental health.

Within the processes of reviewing existing provision, there was a convergence of government policy, professional philosophy and user choice on the shape of future services. In particular, day centres for adults were viewed as only being appropriate for providing short-term rehabilitation or long-term care for those who would not be able to utilise new initiatives or mainstream provision in education or employment. All those patients/clients who could be diverted away from health and social services provision into integrated mainstream services by providing support, would have that option. This approach, it was hoped, would reverse the trend of people with disadvantages being segregated from the rest of society and being stigmatised as patients/clients. Instead, it was hoped that the new approach would promote social inclusion and that the people concerned would simply be viewed as students, trainees or employees similar to the rest of their peers.

As the 1996 publication entitled 'Working it Out' (Pozner et al) states:

> *"The truth is that we simply do not know what is possible, given the availability of more flexible job opportunities and intensive and long-term support. Nevertheless, it is safe to say that the proportion who could work, given the right conditions, is far higher than actually do work at present. The majority have simply never had the chance."*

The drive away from State provision to promoting self-help and community care has been enacted through a number of pieces of legislation including:

The Northern Ireland Mental Health Order 1985
The Community Care Order 1990
The Disability Discrimination Act 1995
The Welfare Reform Bill 1999

Such legislation gave health and social services agencies the statutory approval to diversify and to seek new ways to deliver support for the more disadvantaged in our society.

CASE STUDY: Social Firms in Craigavon and Banbridge Community Health & Social Services Trust

The Craigavon and Banbridge Community Health & Social Services Trust, which came into existence in 1994, was particularly eager to exploit the opportunities that Trust status gave it to restructure and reorganise its services. Through the work of a Community Development Team the Trust had developed strong relations with the voluntary sector and other public agencies, such as the councils and education boards, in their area. It was these relationships which developed into formalised partnerships that provided the springboard into social firms.

There has always been a certain degree of overlap between community development and community enterprise; however, this has yet to reach the stage of integrated strategies. This has been restricted because of the nervousness on both sides. Community groups, for example, are fearful of taking on business proposals because they feel they lack the skills required, and the business community is reluctant to get into partnership with the community sector because it views business in very traditional terms. Some would say, for example, that our society disproportionally values economic development over social development, instead of seeing the strategic links that can be made between the two. As Paul Sweeney (1989) states:

> "There is an artificiality in this dichotomy of dividing social and economic objectives. Few modern successful societies do this, realising that enterprise can be as easily discovered and encouraged in community-based initiatives as well as with financial institutions. Ireland urgently requires a healthy, strong, enabling development strategy contributing to social and economic regeneration, that impacts in need and challenges those with the power to effect progressive change."

The structure changes in the Health Service gave rise to opportunities for community organisations to fulfil Health Service contracts and to develop new health care businesses that the Health Trust could buy into. The Community Work Team enabled these proposals to be developed, and acted as the link between the Trust and the community enterprises that were beginning to emerge. Through networking with other agencies like 'Business in the Community' and 'Community Business', the Community Work Team were also able to help the community sector develop strategic alliances with the private sector.

The Community Work Team saw itself playing a pivotal role in breaking down some of the traditional barriers between the private and voluntary sectors, and they saw the community enterprises and social firms as the ideal vehicles to achieve this. As Paul Sweeney (1989) asserts:

> *"If we make this our starting point and accept Community Development, integrating social and economic objectives, can stand up to the most rigorous cost benefit analysis, then it should be possible for the private sector and the community development sector to marry their respective resources."*

In 1995 the Craigavon and Banbridge Community Health & Social Services Trust joined in a European-funded transnational partnership through the Horizon Programme, to develop services for people with mental health problems, to enable them to re-integrate into the workforce. This project was known as Assessment, Counselling and Coaching in Employment, Placement and Training (ACCEPT). In 1998 the Trust also became a partner in a second European transnational project known as Vocational Opportunities in Training and Employment (VOTE), which looked at similar initiatives for young people with any form of disadvantage or disability. This was funded under the Youthstart Programme. In both these initiatives social firms were to be an element of the scheme. Given that social firms as a concept was relatively unknown in the Irish and British experience, some work had to be undertaken to inform those who may benefit by their development whether they were users, entrepreneurs or statutory and voluntary agencies. It was also important to bed the projects down not just in Northern Ireland as a region, but within localities, using community development principles of networking and working in partnership.

In representing a community development team the value base is centred around working with clients to enable them to improve their own circumstances. The community development approach begins from the premise that if intervention is to succeed, its chances increase significantly if the clients or community are in charge of the process. In short, it is important that we move at their pace and not try and drive the process in the pursuit of our own agency's goals. 'Self-help' however, should not be seen as a method of the State opting out of its responsibilities to its citizens; rather it's about citizens working alongside agencies of the State as equal partners. Taking this type of approach is not unique to the community development speciality within social work, although the casework approach is often restricted by its statutory duties. Adams (1990) highlights this when he states:

> *"It is increasingly common to find social workers who want to get involved in self-help activities, who believe strongly in the principle of moving people towards improving their control over their own circumstances."*

The social firms model has the potential to offer people more control over their own lives, because it has the potential to reintroduce them to society as productive members of the community.

A key element of empowering clients, groups or communities is to conduct effective consultation processes. Too often in the past statutory bodies have only engaged in information sharing exercises, which do not offer communities real opportunities to influence the decision-making process. It is also difficult for community-based groups to engage in effective consultation - not because the process is not genuine - but because the information is produced in an inaccessible format using professional jargon. Preparation for consultation often needs to be undertaken so that those involved can engage meaningfully. This preparation training aims to provide participants with a better understanding of the purpose of the consultation, the process to be followed and in understanding the agency conducting the consultation. From the community's perspective they often believe decisions have already been made even before the consultation is carried out. If agencies do approach consultation in this fashion, the success of their initiatives is likely to be limited because they are not inclusive enough. The initiative will have more chance of success when the views of the community are taken on board to the extent that a real sense of ownership of the process prevails. As the Calouste Gulbenkian Foundation (1975) stated:

> *"The decision-makers could consult much more widely and systematically with the multiplicity of existing community groups and organisations, ranging from advisory and professional bodies, local councils and voluntary welfare*

or interest groups to groups speaking for consumers or mobilised for protest or community action. The purpose would be to thrash out local differences of opinion and reach some degree of consensus."

In order to ensure that community groups could engage in the development of social firms in the locality, the Community Work Team decided to hold a preparatory seminar which would inform them about the opportunities available.

The initial list of invitations was not seen as exhaustive, and at the beginning of the meeting it was made clear that it was not a closed group, others may join at later stages.

At the seminar, those present were given a presentation on social firms, how they developed and what the principles were that underpinned the concept. These included empowering the disadvantaged, integrating people with disabilities or mental health difficulties back into society and diverting people away from care by the State to self-help, when appropriate. Suggestions were also made as to how social firms could be relevant to those present.

Finally, the seminar involved a session on generating ideas. People were asked to discuss any ideas they had which could have potential for developing into social firms. A number of suggestions were proposed at this time and it was agreed to follow these ideas up with relevant groups and individuals. In the follow-up process it quickly emerged that one suggestion, in particular, had potential to grow into a substantial social firm. This involved a partnership with Craigavon Borough Council, ACCEPT and the Trust.

The basic proposal was to establish a company limited by guarantee, entitle 'Tannaghmore Enterprises', which would take over a 100-acre site from the Council, which had been used for tourism and recreation. The Company would manage the site and develop, it not just for its original use, but including business operations such as a retail unit, restaurant and a horticultural production unit. Given the scale of the site and the variety of work opportunities available, it potentially would be able to accommodate large numbers of trainees and employees at the one time. As the partnership had no real business expertise, it was essential to bring such knowledge into the scheme at an early stage. Consultants were recruited following the designing of a detailed brief, and their task was to compile an economic appraisal and business plan for the scheme. Although the consultants were given a significant amount of responsibility, they worked very closely with the partners, to ensure it met with their expectations. As Grove et al (1997) state:

> *"Graumann believes proper market research is vital to setting up and maintaining a business, but warns that even very good consultants who present a fully researched range of options do not absolve management from making momentous decisions."*

Such decisions, however, could not be secured until funding could be attracted for the project. When ordinary businesses are developing an idea they have to secure enough financial assistance either through investors, borrowing, grants or subsidies in order to get established. Social Firms are no different, they will seek support from a number of sources, although purists criticise this approach, accusing such schemes as not being self-sustaining. Grove et al (1997), however, take a different attitude:

> *"We see no moral or philosophical reason why social firms should not operate like any other businesses and take advantage of whatever grants, subsidies, tax breaks or investment opportunities which are going from whatever source. How else do most of our major industries survive and thrive?"*

With this approach in mind, the Partnership looked at a number of funding opportunities that were available at that time. Northern Ireland is probably in a unique funding situation because it has a number of sources from which to draw. In particular, funding from Europe plays a highly significant role through both the Structural Funds, as Northern Ireland up until recently was an Objective One Region, and through the Special Programme for Peace and Reconciliation.

Although Northern Ireland will be an 'Objective One in transition' designation in the next round of Structural Funds, the financial contribution from Europe will still be significant. Employment will be at the centre of most of the programmes following on from the 1997 'Amsterdam Treaty', and the Jobs Summit held later that year in Luxembourg. All Member States have now agreed an integrated European Strategy which has four priorities: employment, adaptability, entrepreneurship and equal opportunities. This strategy recognises the importance of making the workforce inclusive, specifically under the priorities of employability and equal opportunities. Flowing from these priorities, new community initiatives have been designed called 'Equal', which will attempt to develop co-operation in overcoming social exclusion, discrimination and inequalities in relation to employment and the labour market. Initiatives like social firms will be strategically well placed to bid for the funding available, in order to improve the inclusion of people with a disability.

America also plays an important role through The International Fund For Ireland. In more recent times the National Lottery has added to the opportunities for funding. Applications were made to several of these sources for funding, following a successful outcome from the consultant's feasibility study. The proposal had already had a considerable amount of financial support from the Craigavon Council in terms of the 100-acre site on a long-term lease for a nominal sum. The Council also agreed to maintain its current level of investment (£100,000), to maintain the property, and to award the ground maintenance contract to the new Company. With this type of capital and revenue already available, it was in a strong position to attract grants from the main funders.

The Craigavon Borough Council Peace and Reconciliation Programme was the first to show an interest in the project. They agreed to fund the project to the value of £70,000. This finance is sufficient to kick-start the project in a phased approach. The project was launched in June 1999, when fully operational it should employ seventeen people and also provide forty to fifty places for trainees. The employees/trainees will have a range of work opportunities to choose from including: animal husbandry, grounds maintenance, retail sales, security, cleaning, food preparation, administration, marketing and tourism.

VOTE (Vocational Opportunities Through Education)

Although the approach to the establishment of Tannaghmore Enterprises was inclusive, lessons were learned from that process, and before further European applications were submitted it was agreed to look at the processes involved. As a result of this review it was identified that there may be a benefit in establishing a 'Disability Forum' to look at shared issues or problems. The term 'disability' in this context was based on the European model which considers those from a mental health background and those who are economically disadvantaged as 'disabled' people. This Forum was convened and began to discuss what need existed and what services were available to meet these needs. This highlighted not just the gaps in provision but the myriad organisations that are in existence to address some of those needs. Even agencies who were involved in service delivery within the disability arena did not know of all the other services, which suggests that clients would be even less likely to be aware of what is on offer. The Forum then undertook to address both the issue of gaps in provision and the lack of information on the available services. The VOTE project was therefore a response to a gap in provision for young people with a disability leaving school and trying to access further education, training or employment.

Again the partnership model was considered the most appropriate, and this was developed between the Craigavon and Banbridge Community Health & Social Services Trust, Upper Bann Institute of Further Education and ACCEPT/Action Mental Health.

Primarily, the focus of the project is to prepare twenty-eight students for work through a four-element training package and work placements. Plans, however, are also being made to develop a social firm initiative around a catering project, and consultants are currently conducting a feasibility study in conjunction with a private developer.

As can be seen from the above, Europe's contribution to the growth of these local initiatives has been both conceptual and financial. That contribution goes beyond those already mentioned, as through the projects, relationships with European partners were encouraged and developed. A number of transnational conferences and seminars were held to further refine the social firms concept. At these interfaces, discussion took place on shared problems and issues, and contrasts in social policy. From these discussions it emerged that in countries like Germany the benefits system was much more enabling for people with disabilities, in comparison to the United Kingdom model. The biggest inhibitor for people in the United Kingdom taking up employment in social firms, is the benefit system.

The situation at present is, if someone is on the full range of disability benefits available to them, then they would be economically worse off by taking up low-paid jobs in social firms. There is also no provision at present to allow people to sample work, and if it does not suit their needs, return to the same level of benefits as they had prior to taking up work.

Under the Conservative Government of 1979-1997, the benefit system was radically reorganised, making it harder to qualify for certain benefits and more difficult to continue on them. This type of environment created a fear factor for people on disability benefit and carers who could receive associated benefits. The Conservative approach, with the stated aim of taking people off benefits to encourage them back to work, was actually counterproductive in relation to people with a disability. The fact that the Conservative Government also decided against signing up to the European Social Chapter meant that the European experience was largely ignored in the United Kingdom.

When a Labour Government came to power in 1997, they instigated a review of the benefit system, acknowledging there were disadvantages to people with a disability. Also, the Labour Government's attitude to the European Union was more progressive and more consistent with the social democratic mainstream in Europe.

During 1999, the Labour Government have introduced to Parliament a Welfare Reform Bill which they claim will improve the disability benefit system to encourage people to take up employment opportunities within training programmes .

The new Welfare Reform Bill, however, has been heavily criticised by organisations such as Disability Action, who believe that the bill has primarily been a cost-cutting exercise to the value of £750 million. A spokesperson for Disability Action stated that the Government was trying to restrict access to benefits for disabled people, yet they still face discrimination when seeking employment. Disability Action have, however, welcomed the provision within the Bill which creates a 'single gateway' to benefits: *"Providing there is adequate support, this could mean more disabled people having an opportunity to find employment."*

Disabled people themselves, having felt under particular scrutiny following the previous Conservative Government Social Security changes, have viewed with concern Labour's proposal for 'compulsory interviews.' Even the Minister, Allister Darling, has acknowledged the proposals are 'harsh' but, in his opinion, 'justifiable'.

This view, however, was not supported wholeheartedly by the Labour Parliamentary Party as sixty-five Labour MPs voted against the Bill, which has been the biggest rebellion since

Labour took up office in 1997. At the time of writing, the Bill was being passed to the House of Lords where it is expected to face significant amendments.

Disabled people, through their representative bodies, have stated they do want work opportunities: they do, however, feel that there is still a lack of job vacancies and widespread discrimination, and these should have been addressed before the review of benefits. Even when people with disabilities do gain employment they are in low-paid and low-status occupations. The working environments are often not accessible for people with disabilities, and there are limited support services available to counteract these problems.

The Welfare Reform Bill is not the only government initiative which tries to motivate people with disabilities back into the workforce. This is also being looked at under schemes such as 'New Deal' which is the Government's 'big idea' within the Social Security Sector. The Mental Health Foundation, in a briefing Paper on 'Welfare to Work' identifies what the New Deal is supposed to do and the problems it faces when it makes the following points: the New Deal for people with a disability or long-term illness aims to help disabled people currently dependent on benefits back into work. The initiative will include the following measures: innovative programmes, personal advisers; an information campaign, and research and evaluation.

New Deal measures will be ineffective unless mirrored by comprehensive structural reforms to the benefit system, to remove disincentives associated with moving from benefits to work. The Disabled Person's Tax Credit and other changes may not be sufficient to ease transition to work, and there needs to be ongoing review of the relationship between New Deal programmes and the benefits system.

The Mental Health Foundation argue that flexibility is the key to working with people with a disability, and any programme should offer the following: be optional; be tailored to individual need; give participants control of intensity and pace of service; offer long-term and intensive support when required; support a range of outcomes, not just paid employment; genuinely meet employers' needs and be able to accommodate the fluctuating nature of many people's disability.

The Foundation suggests a continuum of service models which the individual could engage with at the appropriate level. Included along that continuum are models such as sheltered work placements, sheltered employment, social firms and co-operatives, supported education and training, access to employment services, job coaching, clubhouses and transitional employment programmes, supported placement scheme and work retention approaches.

Although the concerns of the Mental Health Foundation and others cannot be dismissed, it is too early to evaluate how successful the New Deal is being at affecting change. The Northern Ireland experience to date has been that in the initial stages very few people were taking up the New Deal option. In recent times that has begun to change because the Government is now putting the administrative infrastructure into place to support those people who are willing to give New Deal a chance. In Northern Ireland as well, the programme includes the twenty-five-plus age range, which increases the opportunities available. What is clear at this stage is that the Government is serious about welfare reform, and it is the duty of support and lobby organisations to ensure that any reforms assist people to be included fully in society.

Conclusion

Social firms cannot be a panacea to all the issues which surround providing those with disabilities or mental ill health with a meaningful and productive lifestyle. The concept is in fact one method among many which offer people the opportunity to reintegrate into society and normalise their life experience. The crucial factor for social firms is that they help the client and caring services change the dynamic which operates between them. Instead of having a simple client and professional relationship, it becomes more a partnership where the client gains status through their role as an employee. People are not segregated from the rest of society in Centres which can mainly offer them social and developmental activities, as opposed to them going to a place of employment where they will meet and work with people who have no disability. The ethos of social firms replicates the ethos of community work, because it's about empowerment, it's about allowing people to help themselves, rather than making them dependent on statutory provision, which can be stigmatising.

Although studies such as those conducted by Warner (1985) and Sheppard (1995), show that employment and the social status it affords are key to people's wellbeing, obviously not everything associated with work is necessarily positive. One of the main difficulties, for example, is centred around the attitude of those without a physical or mental disability, towards those who have a disability. As a result of the traditional approach to dealing with clients, that is, segregating them into long-stay units or day centres, society as a whole has been separated from people who are mentally ill or who have a disability. Not surprisingly perhaps, this has led to ignorance and prejudice, and it is often clear that finding work in open employment is difficult for people who are disabled or who have experienced a period of mental ill health. The survey conducted by Manning and White in 1995 for the Royal College of Psychiatrists discovered that 30% of 120 public limited companies would only occasionally, or never employ someone who had suffered a mental health problem.

The development of initiatives such as social firms will help to end the segregation of those who are disadvantaged, and break down ignorance and prejudice. As various social firms become established, only time will tell if they are truly sustainable; however, it is important to have them available as an option. Grove et al (1997) sum it up well when they say:

"The social and psychological value of work, particularly for those with serious mental health problems, transcends its material significance. To meet their needs we require a range of provisions; there is no magic solution. People are different, they have different abilities and different ambitions and they need a range of different solutions."

References

Adams, R (1990) Self Help, Social Work and Empowerment, Macmillan Press, Ltd, London.

Community Work Group, A Study for the Calouste Gulbenkian Foundation (1973) Current Issues in Community Work, Routledge and Kegan Paul Ltd, London.

Department of Health & Social Services (1992) Inspection of Day Services for Adults with a Learning Difficulty in Northern Ireland, HMSO, Belfast.

Department of Health & Social Services (1993) Strategy for the Support of the Voluntary Sector and for Community Development in Northern Ireland, HMSO, Belfast.

Dick, N and Sheppard, G (1995) 'Work and Mental Health a Preliminary Test of Warr's Model in Sheltered Workshops', Journal of Mental Health, Issue 3.

Grove, B, Freudenberg, M, Hardin, A, O'Flynn, D (1997) The Social Firm Handbook, Pavillion, Brighton.

Mannila, S (1996) Social Firms in Europe – Some Practical Aspects, Stakes, Helsinki.

Manning, C, White, P (1995) 'Attitudes of Employers to the Mentally Ill', Psychiatric Bulletin, Issue 19.

NICVA European Unit (1999) Europe and Employment – A Briefing Paper, NICVA, Belfast.

Pozner, Mee Ling Ng, Hammond and Sheppard (1996) Working it Out-Creating Working Opportunities for People with Mental Health Problems, Pavillion, Brighton.

Sweeney, P (1989) 'The Churches and Business Influence on Community Work', page 182-192, in Combat Poverty Agency's Community Work in Ireland, Future Print Ltd, Dublin.

Warner, R (1985) Recovery from Schizophrenia, Routledge and Kegan Paul, London

Wellard, R (1999) 'Revolt in New Labours Ranks Over Disability Reforms', Community Care, 27 May - 2 June 1999.

13

Conclusion

Dr Liz McShane

Background

This book describes the introduction of a community development approach in health and social services within the Craigavon and Banbridge Health & Social Services Trust, and provides a number of varied examples of putting that approach into practice.

Its findings are important and relevant to current policies. Recent Northern Ireland government policy documents such as 'Well into 2000' (1997), 'New TSN' (1998) and 'Fit for the Future: A New Approach' (1999), all require community development approaches to improving health and wellbeing, yet such work is still relatively uncommon within the fields of statutory health and social care.

That community development is still at a relatively early stage of development within mainstream agencies, is reported in the 'Mainstreaming Community Development' document (DHSS, 1999). The Study was commissioned by the Community Development Working Group, a sub-group of the Targeting Health and Social Need Steering Group. The study, which has been published together with the report of the Working Group in the DHSS document, 'Mainstreaming Community Development' (DHSS, 1999), found that most of the Boards and Trusts did not have a stated policy for a community development approach. There was a lack of focus for community development and very few instances of training being provided for staff in this area.

'Mainstreaming Community Development' identifies a number of key issues which need to be addressed in order to further the use of a community development approach to health and social wellbeing. These include: an existing degree of imprecision on the definition of 'community development' and a lack of understanding of a 'community development approach'; incomplete information on current community development projects, and the need to monitor the effectiveness of the community development initiatives which are taking place. There are also issues of supporting the sustainability of community development approaches at agency and community levels, and recognising the critical role of key individuals or 'champions' committed to seeing a community development project through.

Of immediate relevance to this book is the recommendation in 'Mainstreaming Community Development' for "...*structured arrangements for identifying and disseminating examples of good practice on a continuing basis*". This publication can be seen as a dissemination of practice examples to help promote community development aims and practice in health and social services.

Findings

The first three chapters in Part 1 of the book discuss the theoretical frameworks, political and social factors influencing the growth of community work and community development in Northern Ireland, and in particular in the Craigavon and Banbridge area. Chapter 1 traces the history of community development policy and practice in the UK and Northern Ireland. It shows how global, European, UK and local Northern Ireland influences converged in the early 1990s, to produce a climate which was favourable to the introduction of a community development approach into statutory health and social services.

Chapter 2 focuses more specifically on the area served by the Craigavon and Banbridge Health & Social Services Trust. It identifies the factors there which encouraged the growth of community development approaches by statutory health and social services. These factors include: an understanding of, and a commitment to community development within key agencies; the development of an infrastructure for community development; collaboration and networking within the voluntary and community sectors; co-ordination between the voluntary and community sectors and statutory agencies; European Funding Programmes supporting community development work; and local people's experience of community development and of inter-agency work.

Chapter 3 gives information about the context of the Craigavon area as a base for community development work, by presenting a case study of the EU Poverty Three Programme in Brownlow 1989-1994. It draws on comparisons with earlier national programmes in the US and UK and points to the complexities of the work of innovative statutory/community partnerships, set up to tackle deep-rooted problems of poverty and social exclusion. The key need for community education as an active component from the beginning of such a programme is emphasised. The lessons from the evaluation of the Brownlow Programme are very relevant to current debates on moving community development forward through integrated partnerships.

Interpretations of Community Development

The nine chapters in Part 2 of the book give a range of examples from practice, which contribute to a greater understanding of a community development approach in health and social services, and illustrate the value of such an approach for service users, members of local communities, professional staff and their statutory agencies.

While the chapters describe different types of work, there are common themes running through them relating to the aims, concepts and methods of a community development approach in health and social services. The aims of community development work are concerned to tackle inequalities in health and social wellbeing, to enable users of services, or communities affected by services, to have a say in their planning and delivery, and to improve the effectiveness of services in meeting needs. Key concepts in the goals and practice of community development are: empowerment, capacity building, social inclusion, user involvement and partnerships. Interpretations of community development, specific examples of putting these aims and concepts into practice, and challenges of this work are demonstrated in the chapters in Part 2.

Empowerment - Individual and Collective

Chapter 4 on the Community Work Team describes Couto's (1997) stages of empowerment, beginning from the basic point when people discover they are not alone, and begin to define their situation in their own terms, to the development of supportive friendships and people starting to represent themselves and seek solutions to their problems. 'Empowerment' refers both to individuals and to a collective empowerment of groups and communities. Chapter 6 on the work of the Springwell Centre describes the personal empowerment of single parents and women under stress, through a process of empathy, peer support and personal development, which enables women to access services such as adult education, counselling and family therapy. Over a timescale of four to five years, they are able to move on and begin to address issues in their own environment. Thus, for socially excluded groups, personal empowerment is a prerequisite for community development.

Two chapters give examples of collective empowerment and provide models of practice which could be replicated elsewhere. Chapter 9 describes a community training programme in implementing child protection measures and The Children's Order (1995), for community and voluntary groups working with children and young people. Through a cascade model of 'training the trainers', community sector trainees receive training tailored to their needs, in a way which empowers them and gives them ownership of the process. A structure of community reference groups link local networks to the training initiative, maximising participation and using local knowledge.

Chapter 5 refers to an innovative project where community development is facilitated by a rural general practice. It describes a process of empowering the local community through professional staff carrying out a needs assessment, and then supporting the formation and development of a local community development group. Through the group, people came together from scattered rural villages and townlands to identify and address their common needs. In turn, this gave a sense of empowerment and confidence. Improved communications between professionals and the local community about health and social needs, useful feedback on services, and changed relationships and practice all resulted from this process.

Social Inclusion
The concepts of empowerment and social inclusion are clearly linked. Finding ways of empowering socially-excluded individuals and groups is a step towards them making their voice heard and gaining access to services. Tackling social exclusion is demonstrated in work with Travellers, one of the most socially-excluded groups in the Craigavon area. Chapter 7 describes a personal development course which aimed to empower Traveller women by enabling them to express their views on their own lives. Lessons were learned which will assist future work, such as the need for settled people working with Travellers to have a culturally-sensitive approach, to seek informal opportunities to develop self-esteem and where possible, to involve a Traveller facilitator.

Chapter 8 describes the work of a Health Visitor who has been designated to work with Travellers for the past five years. It vividly illustrates the acute health problems and inequalities of health of this group, compared to the settled population. The account shows how, by taking a proactive approach and building up trust 'with Traveller families over a period of time, a professional worker can make mainstream services accessible to them. Both chapters on work with Travellers show the underlying problems of serious deprivation and racism suffered by Travellers, and that any work to overcome their exclusion and tackle their health and social care needs must be in partnership with Travellers themselves.

User Involvement

The empowerment and social inclusion of people with physical and mental disabilities is demonstrated in Chapters 10, 11 and 12. Key aspects of this are encouraging user involvement in decisions about health and social services, in the actual provision of services and in users taking steps themselves to address their own needs. The study in Chapter 10 of a specific project to support people with disabilities to become volunteers in a Volunteer Bureau, shows how with sensitive support and training, people who have previously been 'the helped' can take on the positive role of 'helper'. The responses of those involved show how this increased their confidence, and enabled some of them to begin to look at the possibility of employment.

Chapter 11 describes how staff from statutory services, two mental health voluntary organisations, carers and service users came together in a positive partnership to work on mental health issues. The partnership listened to the views of service users, involved them in positive action to meet their needs, and jointly produced a newsletter for mental health users, carers and staff in the area. This project empowered people who had felt excluded and stigmatised by giving them a voice, and enabled them to participate and move into a positive role within their own community. Chapter 12 sees the development of social firms as an option to empower people to move on from illness and disability to achieve the non-stigmatised mainstream role of employee, rather than patient or client.

Partnerships

A key finding to emerge from all the community development work described is the importance of multidisciplinary and inter-agency work, and the formation of partnerships within and between the statutory, voluntary and community sectors. An indication of the prevalence of joint working is the number of chapters written by more than one person; for example, a total of ten people contributed to the chapter on community development facilitated by a primary care team. Professionals in the statutory services aiming to introduce a community development approach, need to develop the attitudes and skills which enable multidisciplinary working with other professionals and collaboration with other sectors, and to be supported in this by their agencies. Once structures for inter-agency work and partnership working are in place, they can provide an infrastructure of support for community development work in mainstream services.

Chapter 4, on the work of the Community Work Team, describes a range of partnerships with voluntary and community organisations developed by the Team over recent years. A number of these partnerships provided the springboard for specific projects in community development related to the work of health and social services professionals. The Community Work Team has been involved with and supported the Ballyward General Practice initiative, the Lurgan Council for Voluntary Action, the Springwell Centre, the mental health partnership group, the Community Liaison Committee, Craigavon Travellers' Support Group and the Craigavon Social Firms initiative.

The value of partnerships and joint working is to co-ordinate the work of different professionals and organisations, and crucially to bring on board the views of the local community and those receiving services and their carers. This co-ordinated approach can maximise existing resources and enable more resources to be levered into particular projects. It gives a more powerful voice to the combined members than any single group can achieve, and provides an enhanced service for users. Joint working of users and service providers brings about the empowerment of users, and ensures that the services do meet their needs.

Multidisciplinary and inter-agency working are associated with a holistic approach to health and social care needs, which recognises the social and economic factors as well as medical factors affecting health and wellbeing. Professionals involved in such work can experience job satisfaction from perceiving their own role in a holistic way, and gain from the support of a multidisciplinary team.

Barriers to a Community Development Approach

Several writers describe issues or barriers in introducing a different way of working. The experience of the Brownlow Poverty Three Programme described in Chapter 3 shows the structural barriers to full community participation which need to be overcome. The Volunteer Bureau support project and social firms face difficulties with benefit rules, which inhibit involvement for those wishing to move on to more independent living. Practical issues of the need for transport to enable people to participate were encountered by the Volunteer Project and the Mental Health Partnership Group. The latter example shows the need for partnership structures to be able to access independent funding for programme costs, and the subsequent work involved in obtaining charitable status.

All the examples show that professionals engaged in innovative ways of working with users and communities are giving additional time and effort to this. For longer-term sustainability of such work, it needs to be recognised as a legitimate part of their professional role and be built into their work timetable. The support of managers within the agencies is necessary for professional staff to engage effectively with users and the voluntary and community sectors.

In partnership working, community and user groups and health and social services professionals need to perceive each other interacting in different sets of roles and relationships, than those which existed before. They need to deal with the feelings of uncertainty or insecurity which this can engender, and be willing to take risks. This is a process of joint learning and will take time. There is a danger of the community partner being given less recognition than the statutory staff, and conscious efforts need to be made to ensure that this does not happen. There is a need to make efforts to involve users and enable them to continue to participate, and to allow the time for this process. Where professionals are working with socially-excluded groups, it is necessary to be sensitive to cultural differences and to work at people's own pace. Sometimes the prevalent attitudes of the wider society can inhibit the work, for example when seeking to empower people with disabilities.

A book on community development cannot ignore the all-pervading sectarianism, which is part of life in contemporary Northern Ireland. It is almost taken for granted by professionals and community activists, many of whom are accustomed to negotiating around the issue on occasions, for example when community partnerships are formed by groups from different areas. In Chapter 5 the Ballyward General Practice Surgery began with the key advantage of being a 'neutral venue' for all groups from the surrounding mixed area it serves.

Role of the Community Work Team as Part of Mainstream Services

The role of the Community Work Team in Craigavon and Banbridge Trust in enabling the community development work described in this book, is a crucial one. It has continuously promoted the community development approach, even in periods like the 1980s and early '90s, when it was seen as peripheral to mainstream health and social services policy, and at a time of severe resource constraints in health and social services.

The Team has consistently provided support, expertise, funding advice and funds to local voluntary, community and user self-help groups. This includes forming partnerships with such groups as appropriate, and providing basic administrative back-up services when needed. It has consciously worked to build up and support voluntary and community networks, to provide an infrastructure for community development work at local level. In turn, these networks and other local voluntary and community groups are then able to engage with the Trust on its priorities and work. While the link between statutory services and the voluntary sector can be more easily achieved, it can be the means of the health and social services agency carrying out developmental work within smaller community or interest groups.

The relation between the Community Work Team, the Craigavon and Banbridge Community H&SS Trust and the Southern Health & Social Services Board is an important example for other areas on the process of mainstreaming community development work. The Community Work Team has succeeded in establishing a commitment from the Board and Trust to a strategic community development approach, and community development principles and practice as part of mainstream services. Chapter 4 describes the factors behind this achievement, such as the Team's adaptability; its relevance, how it has identified where the Trust's priorities dovetail with community and users' concerns; its innovation in researching new approaches and funding opportunities, and its presentation of an annual business plan.

A further value of the Community Work Team as part of mainstream social and health services has been its capacity to form sound links between different professional staff and encourage multidisciplinary working. In turn, through its established community and voluntary sector links, it has facilitated partnerships between mainstream statutory services and those sectors.

The existence of the Community Work Team is thus seen as a prerequisite for the community development approach to be introduced into mainstream policy, services and funding. It straddles the area between the culture and world of professionals in statutory agencies, and that of people in community and self-help groups. Bringing these two together can involve conflicting values and priorities, as well as differences in language and approach. The Community Work Team can act as a broker and interpreter between the two areas to the benefit of both.

In recent years, the example of Craigavon and Banbridge has been followed in the Eastern Board, where first the North and West Belfast Trust, and then the South and East Belfast Trust have set up community development teams.

Policy and Practice of Community Development

The work described in the book incorporates the criteria of community development as good practice as defined by the Community Development Working Group and the Northern Ireland Regional Strategy for Health and Social Wellbeing 1997-2002 (DHSS, 1996). The criteria are:

- *"The extent to which an approach:- empowers individuals and communities by their active involvement in decisions about their health and social needs and the services provided, and by taking steps to address their needs;*
- *"maximises the participation of service users and makes services more responsive to their need;*
- *"promotes the development of partnerships between health and personal social services professionals, other agencies, voluntary and community groups and local people;*
- *"makes use of local knowledge;*
- *"helps target resources to where they are most needed;*

- *"brings about a sense of local ownership and control;*
- *"strengthens the social fabric and support systems within disadvantaged communities."*

Similarly, a number of the recommendations contained in the 'Mainstreaming Community Development Report' (DHSS, 1999), which aims to promote community development approaches within HSS Boards and Trusts, are relevant to the discussion of these issues in the preceding chapters. The recommendations include: the need to establish links between community development and HPSS Board primary care commissioning; the allocation of resources and inter-agency arrangements; that Trusts be required to show the outcomes from funding for community development; that Trusts set community development aims and targets for each Programme of Care or Department, and define arrangements for the involvement of users and of relevant voluntary and community sector agencies in decisions about service delivery.

The report also points out that the process of community development will take time to embed in the culture of Boards and Trusts, and time to deliver the intended outcomes. A realistic time frame is needed, as there is the need for multidisciplinary working and co-operation.

A further aspect is that the process of community development requires a different way of working with service users and local communities than many professional staff have previously experienced. This will necessitate specific training for some staff, and agency support and help for all those engaged in such initiatives. The Craigavon and Banbridge Trust are supporting one of five projects under the Northern Ireland Policy to Practice pilot programme, organised by the Community Development and Health Network (Northern Ireland) which integrates training and support for staff introducing community development approaches into mainstream work.

Future Development of Community Development Approaches

A number of factors influence the development of the community development approach described in this book. Policy issues which are particularly relevant are: the Government's 'New Targeting Social Need and Promoting Social Inclusion Policy', 1999; the proposals from 'Fit for the Future: A New Approach', 1999; and the 'Compact Between Government and the Voluntary and Community Sector in Northern Ireland', 1998.

The new policy on 'promoting social inclusion' (PSI), will promote joint working between government departments, agencies and public bodies and where appropriate, with partners in the voluntary and community sectors, to identify and tackle problems of social exclusion. This approach of consultation and partnership is also endorsed in the Compact between the Government and the voluntary and community sector. This promotion of inter-agency working and partnerships can clearly go hand in hand with community development approaches.

'Fit for the Future: A New Approach', 1999 proposes a restructuring of health and social services in Northern Ireland. While it will be for the new NI Assembly to determine the final structures of the HPSS, the proposals are that existing Area Boards will be replaced by five Health and Social Care Partnerships and the existing nineteen Trusts reduced to ten. GP Fundholding will be phased out, and Primary Care Co-operatives, formed by primary care professionals coming together, would have a central role in commissioning services for their areas. The role of a rural general practice as a focus for inter-professional working and community development in Chapter 5, provides an example of such a body. However, the policy document refers only to the involvement of professionals, with no mention of inputs from service users or local communities. The example in Ballyward shows that with the facilitation of mainstream community workers, such partnership working can include community and user representatives.

Under the Assembly, structures for Government will include a new Department of Health & Social Services and Public Safety. The Voluntary Activity Unit, currently based in DHSS, which has promoted community development initiatives, will come under the remit of a new Department of Social Development. It is important that this separation does not inhibit efforts to mainstream community development approaches in the health and social services.

Evaluation of Community Development

The Mainstreaming Community Development report has pointed out the importance of rigorous and appropriate evaluation of community development approaches, for their future development within health and social services. The Voluntary Activity Unit has already published 'Monitoring and Evaluation of Community Development in NI' and 'Measuring Community Development in NI. A Handbook for Practitioners' (DHSS, 1996). These, together with the VAU's current work on developing indicators for voluntary sector activity and the Unit's forthcoming conference on community infrastructure, are valuable tools in the process of enabling voluntary and community sector organisations to carry out self-monitoring and self-evaluation of their own work so that they can be in a position to demonstrate the value of their work and help to secure funding to sustain it.

Funding for Community Development

The last five years have seen a major input of funds from Europe into Northern Ireland under the EU Structural Funds and the Special Support Programme for Peace and Reconciliation. These funds aimed to support community infrastructure, social inclusion, capacity building, employability, targeting social need social, and economic regeneration, as well as community relations and peace building. The Peace Funding ends in 2000, and in March 1999, Northern Ireland officially lost its 'Objective 1' status for European funding. However, it has an 'Objective 1 transition' status, with some Structural Funds until 2006, after which date such funding from Europe will decrease. This has serious implications for the sustainability of many local community development initiatives and networks, which have blossomed with European funding support in recent years. Of particular concern are areas of weak community infrastructure in which development work has recently begun the task of building capacity for community development. A wide range of effective community development projects enhancing health and social wellbeing have developed in recent years: it is important that health and social services agencies seek ways of consolidating them and sustaining the work achieved so far.

The task of mainstreaming community development approaches thus becomes more urgent, and the examples and lessons from the work in Craigavon and Banbridge Trust are an important contribution to knowledge of this area. They show what can be achieved and provide models of practice to guide others who are aiming to follow this rewarding route into tackling health and social needs.

References

Couto R A (1997) cited in 'Process-focused, Product-focused Community Planning...' by E Sadan and A Churchman in Community Development Journal, Volume 32, No 1 January.

Department Health & Social Services (1996) Measuring Community Development in NI. A Handbook for Practitioners, DHSS, Belfast.

Department of Health & Social Services (1996) Monitoring and Evaluation of Community Development in NI, DHSS, Belfast.

Department of Health & Social Services (1996) Health and Wellbeing: Into the Next Millennium, Regional Strategy for Health and Social Wellbeing 1997-2002, DHSS, Belfast.
* DHSS (1997) above report now 'Well Into 2000', DHSS, Belfast.

Department of Health and Social Services (1997) Well Into 2000, HMSO, Belfast.

Department of Health and Social Services (1998) New Targeting Social Need: An Agenda for Targeting Social Need and Promoting Social Inclusion in Northern Ireland, HMSO, Belfast.

Department of Health and Social Services (1998) Compact Between Government and the Voluntary and Community Sector in Northern Ireland, HMSO, Belfast.

Department of Health and Social Services (1999) Fit for the Future: A New Approach, HMSO, Belfast.

Department of Health and Social Services (1999) Mainstreaming Community Development in Northern Ireland, DHSS, Belfast.

HMSO, (1996) Children's Order (NI) 1995, HMSO, Belfast.